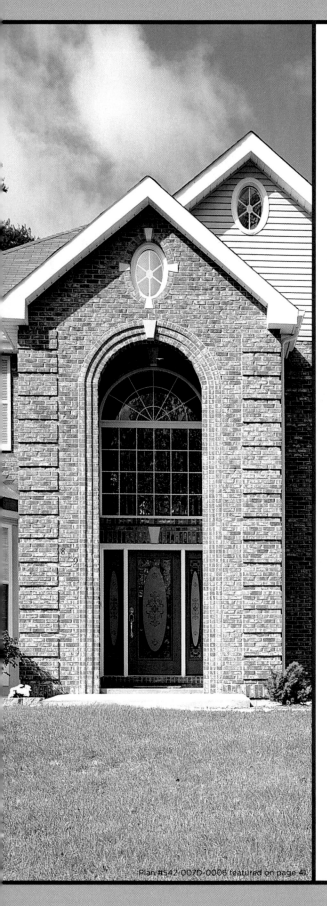

Plan #542-007D-0006 featured on page 41

Contents

LOWE'S LEGACY SERIES

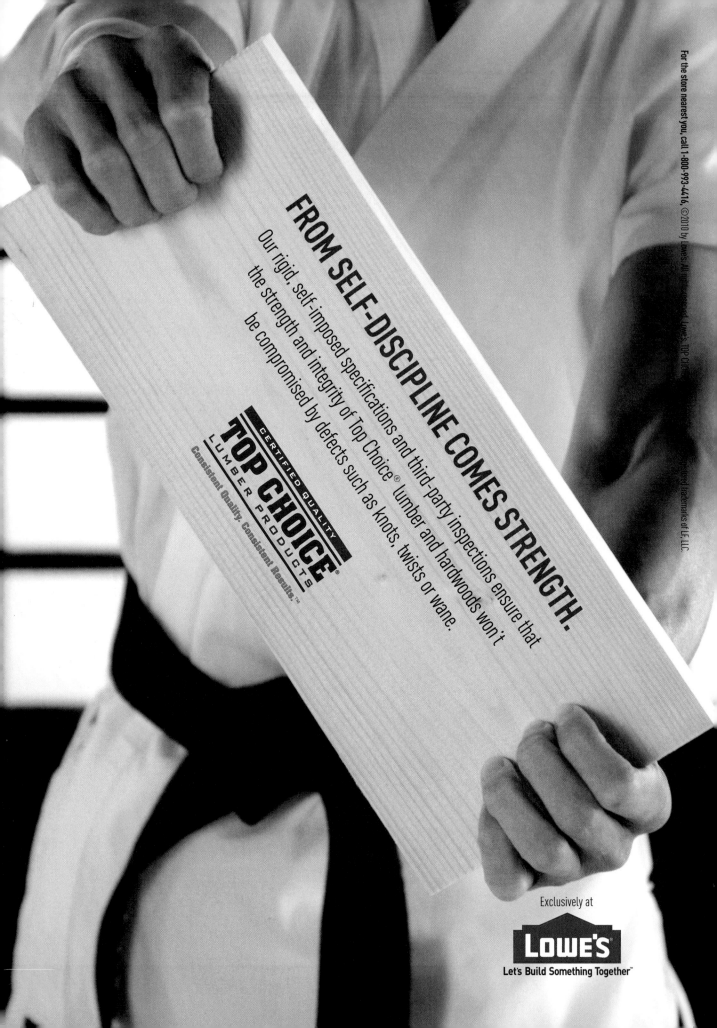

FREE Plan Rebate
See Page 281

FREE Material Take-Off
See Page 284

LUXURY
featuring multi-family plans

Featuring luxury home plans
and multi-family home plans
from Lowe's Legacy Series.

Plan #542-065L-0229 featured on page 25.

COVER HOMES - The home shown on the front cover is Plan #542-007D-0132, featured on page 14, and courtesy of HDA, Inc. The multi-family plan is Plan #542-007D-0094 and is featured on page 250.

LOWE'S LUXURY HOME PLANS
is published by HDA, Inc., 944 Anglum Road, St. Louis, MO, 63042. All rights reserved. Reproduction in whole or in part without written permission of the publisher is prohibited. Printed in the U.S.A. © 2010. Artist drawings and photos shown in this publication may vary slightly from the actual working drawings. Some photos are shown in mirror reverse. Please refer to the floor plan for accurate layout.

ISBN-13: 978-1-58678-145-3

Current Printing

10 9 8 7 6 5 4 3 2

HDA, Inc.
944 Anglum Rd.
St. Louis, Missouri 63042
corporate website - www.hdainc.com

We understand that it is difficult to find blueprints that will meet all your needs. That is why HDA, Inc. is pleased to offer plan modification services.

Thinking About Customizing Your Plan?

If you're like many customers, you may want to make changes to your home plan to make it the dream home you've always wanted. That's where our expert design and modification team comes in. You won't find a more efficient and economic way to get your changes done than by using our design services.

Whether it's enlarging a kitchen, adding a porch or converting a crawl space to a basement, we can customize any plan and make it perfect for your family. Simply create your wish list and let us go to work. Soon you'll have the blueprints for your new home and at a fraction of the cost of hiring an architect!

The HDA Modification Advantage

- We can customize any of the thousands of plans on www.houseplansandmore.com.
- FREE cost estimates for your home plan modifications within 24 hours (Monday-Friday, 8am-5pm CST).
- Average turn-around time to complete the modifications is 2-3 weeks.
- One-on-one design consultations.

3 Easy Steps For Fast Service

1. Visit **www.houseplansandmore.com** to download the modification request form, complete the form and email it to customize@hdainc.com.
2. Fax the completed modification form to 651-602-5050.
3. Call 888-355-5728 for your free estimate.

If you are not able to access the internet, please call 1-877-379-3420 (Monday-Friday, 8am-5pm CST).

Customizing Facts

- The average cost for us to customize a house plan is typically less than 1 percent of the building costs — compare that to the national average of 7 percent of building costs.
- The average modification cost for a home is typically $800 to $1,500 (this does not include the cost of the reproducible blueprint, which is required to make plan changes).
- The average cost to modify a project plan is typically between $200-$500.

Other Helpful Information

- Feel free to include a sketch, or a specific list of changes you'd like to make.
- One of our designers will contact you within 24 hours with your free estimate.
- Upon accepting the estimate, you will need to purchase the reproducible set of plans.
- A contract, which includes a specific list of changes and fees will be sent to you for approval.
- Upon approving the contract, our designers will keep you up to date by emailing or faxing sketches throughout the project.
- Plan can be converted to metric.
- Barrier Free Conversion (accommodating a plan for special needs, transforming your living space for everyone).
- Customizing is also available for project plans, such as sheds, garages, apartment garages and more.

Choosing a home plan is an exciting but difficult task. Many factors play a role in what home plan is best for you and your family. To help you get started, we have pinpointed some of the major factors to consider when searching for your dream home. Take the time to evaluate your family's needs and you will have an easier time sorting through all of the home plans offered in this book.

Budget: The first thing to consider is your budget. Many items take part in this budget, from ordering the blueprints to the last doorknob purchased. When you find your dream home plan, visit your commercial sales specialist at your local Lowe's store to get a cost-to-build estimate to ensure that the finished product will be within your cost range.

Family Lifestyle: After your budget is deciphered, you need to assess you and your family's lifestyle needs. Think about the stage of life you are at now, and what stages you will be going through in the future. Ask yourself questions to figure out how much room you need now and if you will need room for expansion. Are you married? Do you have children? How many children do you plan on having? Are you an empty-nester?

Incorporate in your planning any frequent guests you may have, including elderly parents, grandchildren or adult children who may live with you.

Does your family entertain a lot? If so, think about the rooms you will need to do so. Will you need both formal and informal spaces? Do you need a gourmet kitchen? Do you need a game room and/or a wet bar?

Floor Plan Layouts: When looking through our home plans, imagine yourself walking through the house. Consider the flow from the entry to the living, sleeping and gathering areas. Does the layout ensure privacy for the master bedroom? Does the garage enter near the kitchen for easy unloading? Does the placement of the windows provide enough privacy from any neighboring properties? Do you plan on using furniture you already have? Will this furniture fit in the appropriate rooms? When you find a plan you want to purchase, be sure to picture yourself actually living in it.

> **Experts in the field suggest that the best way to determine your needs is to begin by listing everything you like or dislike about your current home.**

Exterior Spaces: There are many different home styles ranging from Traditional to Contemporary. Flip through and find which style most appeals to you and the neighborhood in which you plan to build. Also think of your site and how the entire house will fit on this site. Picture any landscaping you plan on incorporating into the design. Using your imagination is key when choosing a home plan.

Choosing a home plan can be an intimidating experience. Asking yourself these questions before you get started on the search will help you through the process. With our large selection of multiple styles we are certain you will find your dream home in the following pages.

The Lowe's Legacy Series

Leg·a·cy: Something that is handed down or remains for generations

HDA, Inc. is proud to introduce to you the Lowe's Legacy Series. The home plans in this collection carry on the Lowe's tradition of quality and expertise, and will continue to do so for many generations.

Choosing a home plan can be a daunting task. With the Legacy Series, we will set your mind at ease. Selecting a plan from this group will ensure a home designed with the Lowe's standard of excellence, creating a dream home for you and your family.

This collection of Legacy Series plans includes our most popular luxury home plans. Browse through the pages to discover a home with the options and special characteristics you need.

Along with one-of-a-kind craftsmanship, all Legacy Series home plans offer industry-leading material lists. These accurate material lists will save you a considerable amount of time and money, providing you with the quantity, dimensions and descriptions of the major building materials necessary to construct your home. You'll get faster and more accurate bids from your contractor while saving money by paying for only the materials you need.

The Lowe's Legacy Series is the perfect place to start your search for the home of your dreams. You will find the expected beauty you want and the functional efficiency you need, all designed with unmatched quality.

Turn the page and begin the wonderful journey of finding your new home.

Photos clockwise from top: 542-021D-0019, page 28; 542-053D-0017, page 48; 542-051L-0246, page 33; 542-007D-0063, page 38.

Luxury Home Building Trends

Top home design building trends homeowners want in their new homes today.

*P*icture your dream home, what does it include? Would you love an outdoor fireplace? Or, do you prefer relaxing in a marble whirlpool tub? These features and more are available for every homeowner today. But, what are the home design trends that are requested from builders over and over?

Plan #542-007D-0132, see page 14.

Plan #542-065L-0011, see page 63.

1. Luxurious Kitchens and Baths

Homeowners are demanding more functional space in the kitchen. Many new kitchen home designs include a coffee space, baking area, butler's pantry or casual snack bar. Multiple islands are also popular. One island may feature a sink and dishwasher while another may contain a stove. Separating kitchen tasks allows multiple cooks in the kitchen while still maintaining function.

When it comes to the bathroom, homeowners are drawn to a home design with "his and her" everything. Whether it's closets, vanities or separate baths. When it comes to luxury features, waterfall tubs and fireplaces top the list.

2. Flexible Floor Plans

Families are yearning for more seamless spaces that allow movement to flow from the indoors out. Sliding and pocket doors help achieve this between rooms and other spaces. Other increasingly popular options are home designs featuring hobby spaces, home offices, and bonus or flex spaces. These types of spaces adapt to the needs of today's family.

Plan #542-013L-0053, see page 16.

3. Light-Filled Floor Plans

Natural lighting from skylights, three-season rooms and covered porches are growing in popularity among new home designs. Many of these spaces are now being outfitted with outdoor kitchens, fireplaces, sophisticated sinks and grills helping to draw the family outdoors for more meals and relaxation time.

Plan #542-072L-0025, see page 106.

4. Street Appeal

Forget the cookie cutter homes of the past, or garage dominated styles you see in so many neighborhoods. Home designs that use color and architectural variety are making a comeback.

Plan #542-021D-0019, see page 28.

5. Storage, storage and more storage!

Dressing rooms, walk-in closets and built-in cabinets are musts for all home designs now. Even oversized garages are replacing their smaller counterparts of the past, perfect for large SUVs, boats and storage.

Plan #542-072L-0030, see page 72.

6. Earth-friendly homes

Everyone is "going green" and builders are taking notice. Biodegradable materials and green building techniques are being requested by more and more consumers who are conscious of their surroundings and their well-being.

Plan #542-051L-0544, see page 10.

Amazing Curb Appeal

- 2,887 total square feet of living area
- Energy efficient home with 2″ x 6″ exterior walls
- A cozy hearth room shares a prominent see-through fireplace with the great room offering the perfect spot for casual relaxation
- Double doors off the entry hall lead into a secluded and handsome study with a built-in desk and bookshelves
- The relaxing owner's suite offers a generous walk-in closet, double-bowl vanity, amazing walk-in shower and a spa-style tub to soak your cares away
- 4 bedrooms, 2 1/2 baths, 4-car garage
- Walk-out basement foundation

Second Floor
1,437 sq. ft.

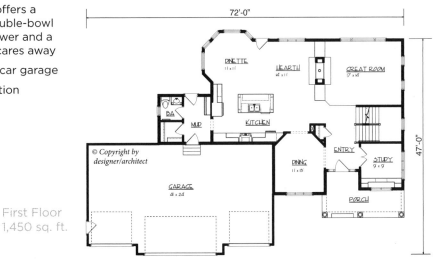

First Floor
1,450 sq. ft.

Luxurious Details Abound

- 3,687 total square feet of living area
- Energy efficient home with 2" x 6" exterior walls
- A magnificent circular staircase winds down to greet you as you enter this Tuscan style home
- The two-story ceiling and fireplace flanked by built-in cabinets in the great room create an atmosphere that's perfect for entertaining
- The spacious kitchen features a large eat-in island and direct access to the formal dining room and laundry area
- 4 bedrooms, 3 1/2 baths, 3-car side entry garage
- Walk-out basement foundation

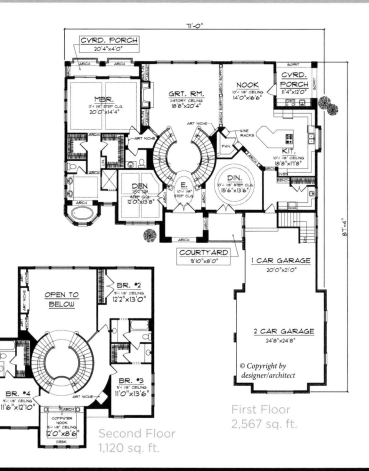

First Floor
2,567 sq. ft.

Second Floor
1,120 sq. ft.

To Order See Page 288 or Call Toll-Free 1-877-379-3420

Sophisticated Ranch With Split Bedrooms

- 2,808 total square feet of living area

- An impressive front exterior showcases three porches for quiet times

- Large living and dining rooms flank an elegant entry

- Bedroom #3 shares a porch with the living room and a spacious bath with bedroom #2

- Vaulted master bedroom enjoys a secluded screened porch and sumptuous bath with corner tub, double vanities and huge walk-in closet

- Living room can easily convert to an optional fourth bedroom

- 3 bedrooms, 2 1/2 baths, 3-car side entry garage

- Basement foundation

92'-4"

64'-8"

Breakfast 16-4x12-5

Patio

Screened Porch 10-4x14-0

MBr 19-0x14-0 vaulted

Kitchen 12-10x13-4

Great Rm 19-0x19-6 vaulted

Br 2 16-6x12-0

Hall

Hall

Entry

Br 3 12-0x13-0

Laundry

Dining 13-0x17-0

Living 13-0x16-10

Porch

Porch

Porch

Garage 20-4x29-4

© Copyright by designer/architect

Rich Facade Adds Warmth And Charm

- 4,562 total square feet of living area
- The cozy hearth room and master bedroom showcase tray ceilings and moldings
- A dressing area, deluxe bath and extra-large walk-in closet crown the master bedroom
- The kitchen with island opens to the breakfast and hearth rooms for an open atmosphere
- 4 bedrooms, 3 1/2 baths, 2-car side entry garage, 1-car garage
- Basement foundation

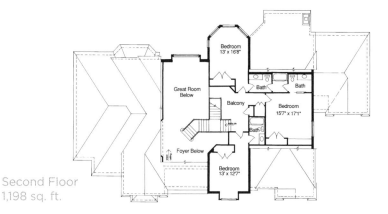

Second Floor
1,198 sq. ft.

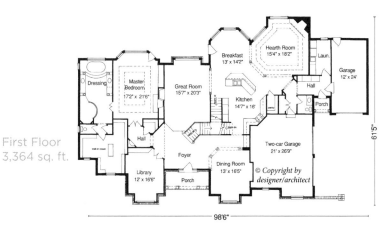

First Floor
3,364 sq. ft.

Stone and Brick Combine

- 4,288 total square feet of living area
- The master bedroom features a deluxe bath with a double vanity, large tub, his and her walk-in closets, and a linen closet
- The hearth room offers a great amount of light and a fireplace that serves as a cozy gathering area
- Each bedroom is spacious in size and has its own walk-in closet
- 4 bedrooms, 3 1/2 baths, 3-car side entry garage
- Basement foundation

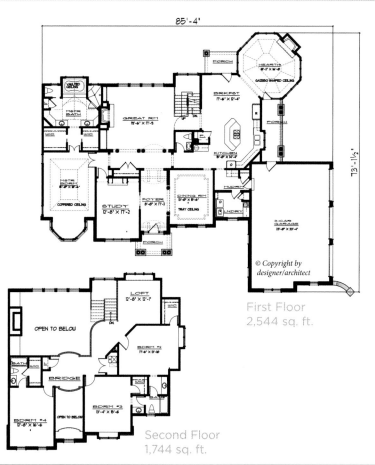

First Floor
2,544 sq. ft.

Second Floor
1,744 sq. ft.

Elegant, Stylish And Sophisticated

- 3,861 total square feet of living area
- Detailed brickwork surrounding the arched windows and quoined corners create a timeless exterior
- Two-story great room has a large fireplace, flanking bookshelves, massive window wall and balcony overlook
- The state-of-the-art kitchen has an island cooktop, built-in oven/microwave oven, large pantry, menu desk and opens to the breakfast and hearth rooms
- A coffered ceiling, bay window, two walk-in closets and a huge bath adorn the master bedroom
- 4 bedrooms, 3 1/2 baths, 3-car side entry garage
- Walk-out basement foundation

First Floor
2,797 sq. ft.

Second Floor
1,064 sq. ft.

© Copyright by designer/architect

Fabulous Courtyard

- 2,854 total square feet of living area

- Energy efficient home with 2″ x 6″ exterior walls

- The elegant entry leads into the quiet great room that is perfect for relaxing with family or partying with friends

- The stunning kitchen features a walk-in pantry, snack bar island and opens to the casual nook and formal dining room

- A lovely three-season porch allows you to enjoy the great outdoors in any weather

- 4 bedrooms, 2 1/2 baths, 3-car side entry garage

- Walk-out basement foundation

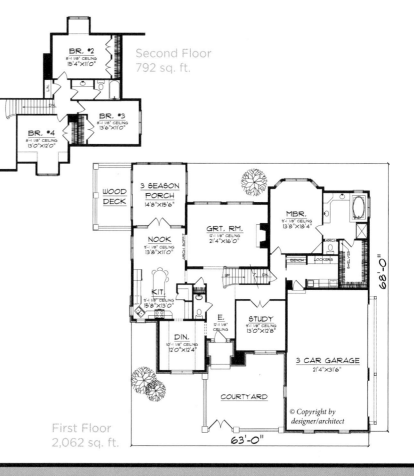

Second Floor
792 sq. ft.

First Floor
2,062 sq. ft.

© Copyright by designer/architect

Bright, Cheerful Windows

- 2,461 total square feet of living area
- The cooktop island in the kitchen has ample counterspace for easy food preparation and connects to the cozy hearth room
- Luxurious master suite has a large closet with conveniently separated hanging areas
- The covered deck/screened porch with vaulted ceiling creates a great outdoor gathering area
- The optional second floor has an additional 518 square feet of living area
- 3 bedrooms, 3 1/2 baths, 3-car side entry garage
- Basement foundation

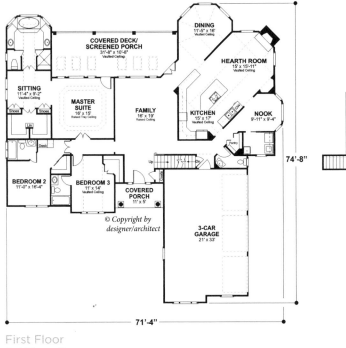

First Floor
2,461 sq. ft.

Optional
Second Floor

Luxury Ranch Home With Subtle Craftsman Style

- 3,196 total square feet of living area
- Energy efficient home with 2″ x 6″ exterior walls
- The cozy great room has a center fireplace flanked by bookshelves
- Double doors off the entry lead to a secluded study perfect for a home office
- The first floor owner's suite has a luxury bath and walk-in closet
- 4 bedrooms, 2 1/2 baths, 3-car garage
- Walk-out basement foundation

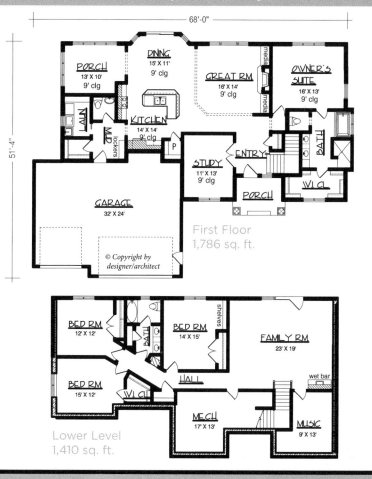

Entry Colonnade, Circle-Top Windows And Columns

- 2,869 total square feet of living area
- Foyer, flanked by columned living and dining rooms, leads to the vaulted family room with a fireplace and twin sets of French doors
- The master bedroom has private access to a large bath featuring two sinks, two closets and a whirlpool tub
- 10' ceilings on the first floor and 9' ceilings on the second floor
- 4 bedrooms, 3 baths, 2-car rear entry garage
- Slab foundation, drawings also include basement and crawl space foundations

Elegant Country Home

- 3,281 total square feet of living area
- Energy efficient home with 2″ x 6″ exterior walls
- The master bedroom is a luxurious retreat with two walk-in closets and a deluxe bath including a whirlpool tub in a bay window
- The kitchen features a cooktop island with eating bar and opens to the nook with access onto the rear porch
- Bedrooms #2 and #3 each feature a cozy window seat and share a Jack and Jill bath
- 4 bedrooms, 3 1/2 baths, 3-car side entry garage
- Basement foundation

Second Floor
1,173 sq. ft.

First Floor
2,108 sq. ft.

© Copyright by designer/architect

Outstanding Floor Plan For Year-Round Entertaining

- 2,597 total square feet of living area
- Large U-shaped kitchen features an island cooktop and breakfast bar
- The entry and great room are enhanced by a sweeping balcony
- Bedrooms #2 and #3 share a bath, while bedroom #4 has a private bath
- The vaulted great room includes transomed arch windows
- 2" x 6" exterior walls available, please order plan #542-007E-0001
- 4 bedrooms, 3 1/2 baths, 2-car side entry garage
- Walk-out basement foundation, drawings also include crawl space and slab foundations

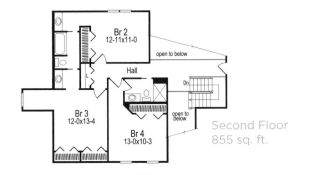

Second Floor
855 sq. ft.

First Floor
1,742 sq. ft.

LOWE'S
LEGACY
SERIES

Pleasing Covered Front Porch

- 3,000 total square feet of living area

- The cheerful kitchen has a double-bowl sink in the island, a large pantry and opens up nicely to the dinette area

- The centralized fireplace separates the hearth and great rooms, warming the home from both sides

- The relaxing owner's bedroom offers a generous closet, double-bowl vanity, amazing walk-in shower and a spa-like tub to soak your cares away

- 4 bedrooms, 2 1/2 baths, 3-car garage

- Walk-out basement foundation

Second Floor
1,429 sq. ft.

First Floor
1,571 sq. ft.

© Copyright by
designer/architect

Width: 70'-0"
Depth: 49'-0"

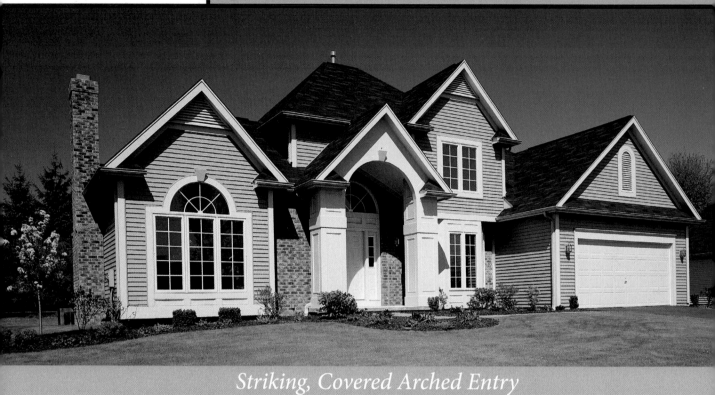

Striking, Covered Arched Entry

- 1,859 total square feet of living area
- Fireplace highlights the vaulted great room
- Master bedroom includes a large closet and private bath
- The kitchen adjoins the breakfast room providing easy access to the outdoors
- 3 bedrooms, 2 1/2 baths, 2-car garage
- Basement foundation

Second Floor
789 sq. ft.

Br 2
10-8x11-3

MBr
11-10x17-2

Dn

open to below

Br 3
11-8x10-2

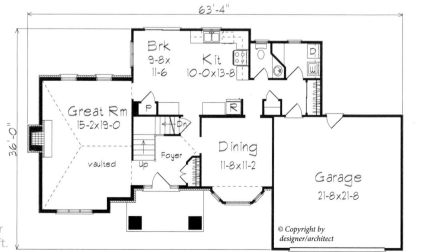

63'-4"

36'-0"

Brk
9-8x 11-6

Kit
10-0x13-8

Great Rm
15-2x19-0

vaulted

Up

Foyer

Dining
11-8x11-2

Garage
21-8x21-8

First Floor
1,070 sq. ft.

© Copyright by designer/architect

LOWE'S
LEGACY
SERIES

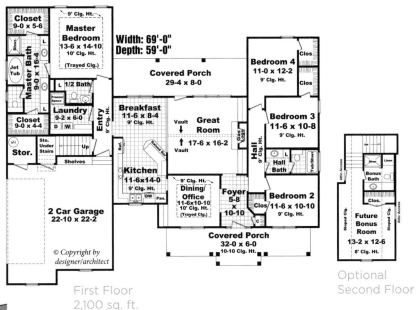

Welcoming Porch

- 2,100 total square feet of living area

- The vaulted great room enjoys the warmth of a gas fireplace flanked by shelves

- Every bedroom features a walk-in closet helping to keep everything organized

- Shelves and extra storage can be found in the garage

- Bonus room above the garage has an additional 317 square feet of living area

- 4 bedrooms, 2 1/2 baths, 2-car side entry garage

- Slab foundation, drawings also include basement and crawl space foundations

Width: 69'-0"
Depth: 59'-0"

First Floor
2,100 sq. ft.

Optional
Second Floor

Stylish Craftsman Symmetry

- 2,715 total square feet of living area

- Energy efficient home with 2" x 6" exterior walls

- The cheerful kitchen has a double-bowl sink in the island, a large corner pantry and opens up to the cheerful dining area

- Double doors off the entry hall lead to a sophisticated study with access to the front covered wrap-around porch

- The owner's suite has an optional fireplace and offers a generous closet and a private bath with a double-bowl vanity, amazing walk-in shower and a whirlpool tub

- 4 bedrooms, 2 1/2 baths, 4-car garage

- Walk-out basement foundation

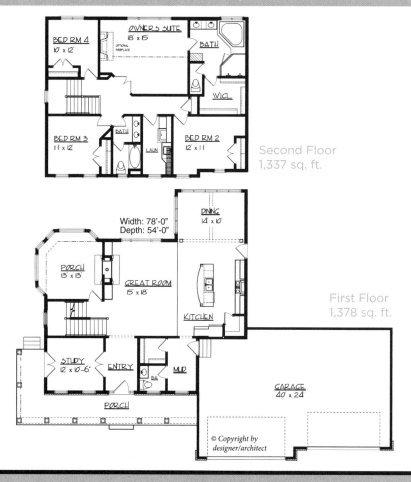

Second Floor
1,337 sq. ft.

First Floor
1,378 sq. ft.

© Copyright by designer/architect

LOWE'S
LEGACY
SERIES

Traditional European Motif

- 3,664 total square feet of living area

- A delightful pub and informal dining area invites family members and guests to relax and enjoy the good times

- Decorative columns define the foyer, formal dining room and great room

- Boasting a tray ceiling treatment, the master bedroom showcases a bath with a whirlpool tub, double-bowl vanity and large walk-in closet

- 4 bedrooms, 2 1/2 baths, 3-car side entry garage

- Basement foundation

Second Floor
1,167 sq. ft.

Bedroom
14' x 17'9"

Bedroom
13'9" x 13'6"

Balcony

Bath

Open to Below

Bedroom
13'2" x 14'2"

walk-in closet

walk-in closet

Patio

Kitchen
14'6" x 14'6"

Informal Dining
15'2" x 18'6"

Pub

Great Room
22'3" x 19'

12' ceiling height

Master Bedroom
17'6" x 13'2"

Laun.

Foyer

walk-in closet

Dining Room
14'6" x 15'6"

Library
11'6" x 15'7"

Three Car Garage
20'8" x 33'5"

Porch

13' ceiling height

© Copyright by designer/architect

First Floor
2,497 sq. ft.

65'

74'10"

Fountain Graces Entry

- 2,397 total square feet of living area

- Covered entrance with fountain leads to the double-door entry and foyer

- Kitchen features two pantries and opens into the breakfast and family rooms

- Master bath features a huge walk-in closet, electric clothes carousel, double-bowl vanity and corner tub

- 3 bedrooms, 2 1/2 baths, 2-car garage

- Slab foundation

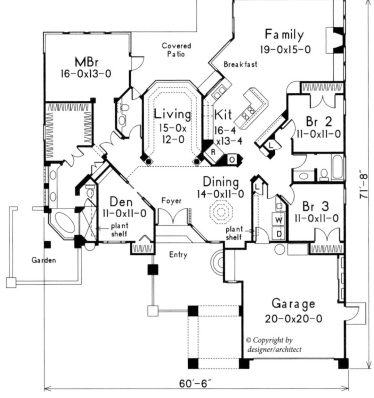

LOWE'S
LEGACY
SERIES

Traditional Home Has Character Of Days Gone By

- 2,445 total square feet of living area

- A dramatic, skylighted foyer preludes the formal, sunken living room that includes a stunning corner fireplace

- A built-in desk and a pantry mark the smartly designed kitchen that opens to the breakfast room and beyond to the family room

- Sunken and filled with intrigue, the family room features a fireplace plus French doors opening to the backyard deck

- 4 bedrooms, 2 1/2 baths, 3-car garage

- Basement foundation

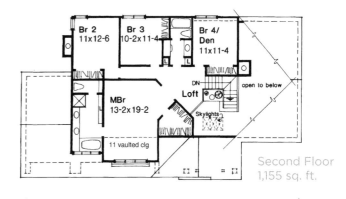

Second Floor
1,155 sq. ft.

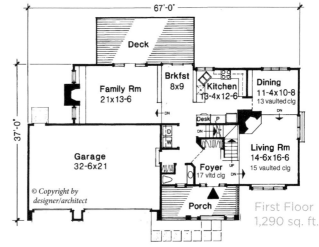

First Floor
1,290 sq. ft.

Plan #542-021D-0019 • Price Code F

Distinctive Two-Level Porch

- 2,605 total square feet of living area
- Energy efficient home with 2" x 6" exterior walls
- Master bedroom boasts a sloped ceiling and transom picture window
- Large kitchen features appliances set in between brick dividers and a beamed ceiling
- Living room features built-in bookcases, fireplace and a raised tray ceiling
- 4 bedrooms, 2 1/2 baths, 2-car side entry garage
- Slab foundation, drawings also include crawl space and basement foundations

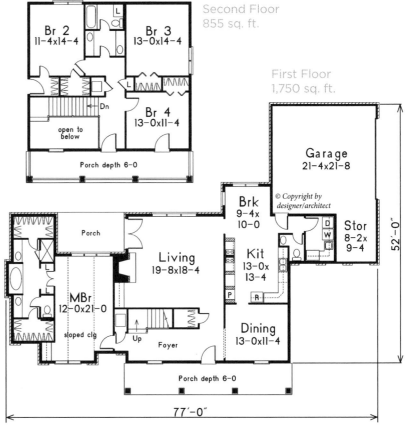

Second Floor
855 sq. ft.

First Floor
1,750 sq. ft.

© Copyright by designer/architect

Br 2
11-4x14-4

Br 3
13-0x14-4

Br 4
13-0x11-4

open to below

Porch depth 6-0

Garage
21-4x21-8

Brk
9-4x 10-0

Stor
8-2x 9-4

Porch

Living
19-8x18-4

Kit
13-0x 13-4

MBr
12-0x21-0

sloped clg

Dining
13-0x11-4

Up
Foyer

Porch depth 6-0

52'-0"

77'-0"

High-Styled Compact Plan

- 2,356 total square feet of living area

- Impressive arched and mullioned window treatment embellishes the entrance and foyer

- Bedroom #4 is located above the side entry garage and has access to the attic

- Full-size laundry facility

- Adjoining family room, breakfast area and kitchen form an extensive living area

- 4 bedrooms, 2 1/2 baths, 2-car side entry garage

- Basement foundation

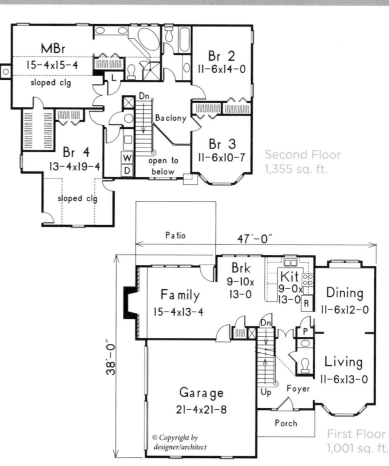

Rambling Ranch Has Luxurious Master Bedroom

- 2,523 total square feet of living area
- Entry with high ceiling leads to massive vaulted great room with wet bar, plant shelves, pillars and fireplace with a harmonious window trio
- Elaborate kitchen with bay and breakfast bar adjoins the morning room with a fireplace-in-a-bay
- Vaulted master bedroom features a fireplace, book and plant shelves, large walk-in closet and double baths
- 3 bedrooms, 2 baths, 3-car garage
- Basement foundation, drawings also include crawl space and slab foundations

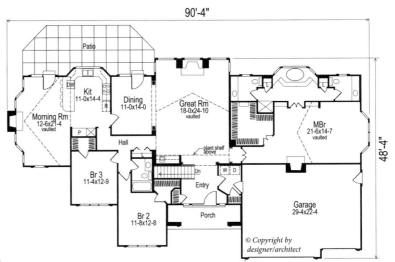

Distinctive Facade

- 2,665 total square feet of living area
- The fireplace provides a focus for family living by connecting the central living quarters
- The abundance of windows, combined with vaulted ceilings, gives this plan a spacious feel
- The large vaulted sun room opens to the kitchen
- Master bedroom features a huge walk-in closet, vaulted ceiling and luxurious bath facilities
- Bonus room on the second floor is included in the total square footage
- 3 bedrooms, 2 1/2 baths, 2-car side entry garage
- Crawl space foundation

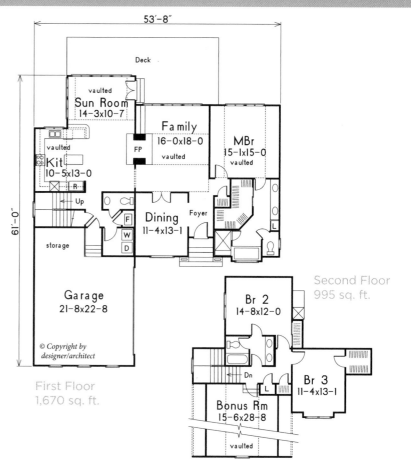

Stunning Craftsman Influence

- 2,697 total square feet of living area
- Energy efficient home with 2" x 6" exterior walls
- A popular porch space shares a see-through fireplace with the great room offering the perfect spot for casual relaxation
- Double doors off the entry hall lead into a secluded and handsome study with plenty of privacy when working from home
- All the bedrooms are located on the second floor for convenient family living
- 4 bedrooms, 2 1/2 baths, 3-car garage
- Walk-out basement foundation

Second Floor
1,314 sq. ft.

Width: 64'-0"
Depth: 54'-0"

First Floor
1,383 sq. ft.

© Copyright by designer/architect

Every Bedroom Has A Walk-In Closet

- 3,099 total square feet of living area
- Energy efficient home with 2″ x 6″ exterior walls
- A see-through fireplace warms both the formal living room and casual family room
- The chef of the family will love this gourmet kitchen complete with an abundance of counterspace, a stovetop island and walk-in pantry
- The nook/sun room with access to a screen porch allows the family to enjoy the great outdoors all year long
- 4 bedrooms, 2 1/2 baths, 3-car garage
- Basement foundation

Second Floor
956 sq. ft.

First Floor
2,143 sq. ft.

Two-Story Bay Window Adds Appeal

- 2,583 total square feet of living area
- Triple-gabled entrance with door sidelights
- Prominent double bay windows add dimension and light
- Convenient rear stairs
- Master bedroom has a private bath with corner tub surrounded by windows, walk-in closet and coffered ceiling
- Bonus room above the garage, which is included in the square footage, converts to a fifth bedroom or an activity center
- 4 bedrooms, 2 1/2 baths, 2-car side entry garage
- Basement foundation

Br 4/ Sitting
10-0x11-6

Br 3
13-6x11-2

Bonus Rm
21-8x14-0
sloped clg

MBr
17-6x13-6
tray clg

Dn

Br 2
13-6x10-0

Second Floor
1,367 sq. ft.

Deck

Family
22-0x13-6

Up

Kit/Brk
13-6x15-6

W
D

Living
14-0x11-6

Dn

P   R

Garage
21-8x19-8

Foyer

Dining
13-6x11-6

© Copyright by
designer/architect

Porch

First Floor
1,216 sq. ft.

29'-0"

62'-0"

Craftsman Charm In A Luxury Size

- 3,126 total square feet of living area
- Energy efficient home with 2" x 6" exterior walls
- A kitchen island featuring a double sink and space for casual dining is just steps away from the dinette and porch
- Perfect for entertaining, the lower level offers a large casual family room and billiards space
- A large and open entry greets guests upon arrival
- 3 bedrooms, 2 1/2 baths, 3-car garage
- Walk-out basement foundation

Width: 68'-0"
Depth: 44'-0"

First Floor
1,705 sq. ft.

© Copyright by designer/architect

Lower Level
1,421 sq. ft.

Outdoor Covered Deck Warmed By Fireplace

- 3,171 total square feet of living area

- An enormous walk-in closet is located in the master bath and dressing area

- The great room, breakfast area and kitchen combine with 12' ceilings to create an open feel

- The optional lower level has an additional 1,897 square feet of living area and is designed for entertaining featuring a wet bar with seating, a billiards room, large media room, two bedrooms and a full bath

- 3 bedrooms, 2 1/2 baths, 3-car side entry garage

- Walk-out basement foundation, drawings also include basement foundation

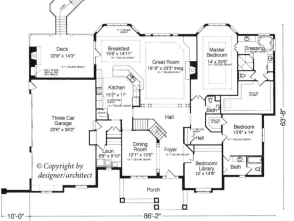

First Floor
3,171 sq. ft.

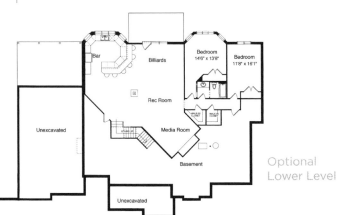

Optional Lower Level

Formal Arched Entry Leads To Convenient Living

- 2,401 total square feet of living area

- Striking front facade with handsome main entry and brick quoins

- Master bedroom has an elegant double-door entry, two walk-in closets and a deluxe bath

- Full bay windows located on both floors create a great view from the rear of this home

- Spacious kitchen features a vaulted ceiling, double pantry, a large work island and planning center

- 3 bedrooms, 2 1/2 baths, 2-car garage

- Basement foundation, drawings also include slab and crawl space foundations

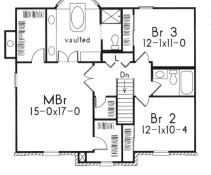

Second Floor
1,046 sq. ft.

Br 3
12-1x11-0

vaulted

MBr
15-0x17-0

Br 2
12-1x10-4

First Floor
1,355 sq. ft.

56'-0"

Patio

Family
19-7x13-7

Brk
9-9x
13-7

Kit
13-6x13-7
vaulted

W
D

36'-0"

Living
13-4x13-6

Dining
12-1x12-11

Garage
19-8x21-6

Porch

© Copyright by
designer/architect

Distinctive Two-Level Living

- 3,138 total square feet of living area
- Impressive staircase descends into the large entry and through double-doors to the study
- The private dining room is spacious and secluded
- Master bedroom, family and laundry rooms are among the many generously sized rooms
- Three large bedrooms, two baths and four walk-in closets compose the second floor
- 4 bedrooms, 3 1/2 baths, 2-car side entry garage
- Basement foundation

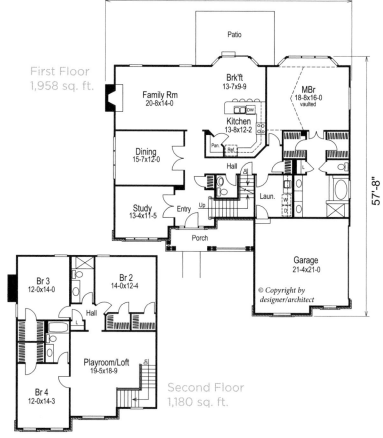

First Floor
1,958 sq. ft.

56'-4"

57'-8"

Patio

Family Rm 20-8x14-0

Brk'ft 13-7x9-9

MBr 18-8x16-0 vaulted

Kitchen 13-8x12-2

Dining 15-7x12-0

Hall

Study 13-4x11-5

Entry

Up

Laun.

Porch

Garage 21-4x21-0

© Copyright by designer/architect

Br 3 12-0x14-0

Br 2 14-0x12-4

Hall

Playroom/Loft 19-5x18-9

Br 4 12-0x14-3

Second Floor
1,180 sq. ft.

To Order See Page 288 or Call Toll-Free 1-877-379-3420

Plan #542-065L-0214 • Price Code F

LOWE'S LEGACY SERIES

Interesting Angles

- 3,809 total square feet of living area
- Entertain guests with a formal dining room, extra-large great room, exciting music room and enchanting rear patio
- A first floor master bedroom pampers the homeowner with its luxurious dressing area and large walk-in closet
- Three additional bedrooms are located on the second floor and enjoy walk-in closets and private bath access
- 4 bedrooms, 3 1/2 baths, 3-car side entry garage
- Basement foundation

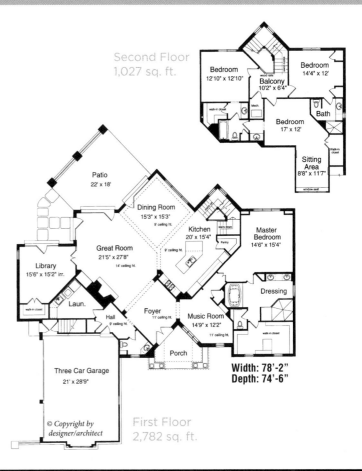

Second Floor 1,027 sq. ft.

Bedroom 12'10" x 12'10"
Bedroom 14'4" x 12'
Balcony 10'2" x 6'4'
Bath
Bedroom 17' x 12'
Sitting Area 8'8" x 11'7"

Patio 22' x 18'
Dining Room 15'3" x 15'3"
Kitchen 20' x 15'4"
Master Bedroom 14'6" x 15'4"
Great Room 21'5" x 27'8"
Library 15'6" x 15'2" irr.
Dressing
Laun.
Hall
Foyer
Music Room 14'9" x 12'2"
Porch
Three Car Garage 21' x 28'9"
© Copyright by designer/architect

Width: 78'-2"
Depth: 74'-6"

First Floor 2,782 sq. ft.

Popular Ranch With Lower Level

- 3,918 total square feet of living area
- Energy efficient home with 2″ x 6″ exterior walls
- Stone decorates the facade of this elegant ranch home
- A bay window accents the quiet study, deluxe owner's suite and charming dinette
- An open family room connects to the billiards area complete with a bar, making a lower level perfect for entertaining
- 3 bedrooms, 2 1/2 baths, 3-car garage
- Basement foundation

First Floor
2,228 sq. ft.

Lower Level
1,690 sq. ft.

© Copyright by designer/architect

LOWE'S
LEGACY
SERIES

Irresistible Grandeur

- 2,624 total square feet of living area

- Dramatic two-story foyer opens to a bayed dining room through a classic colonnade

- Magnificent great room with 18' ceiling is brightly lit with palladian windows

- Master bedroom includes a bay window, walk-in closets, plant shelves and a sunken bath

- 4 bedrooms, 2 1/2 baths, 2-car side entry garage

- Basement foundation

Second Floor
850 sq. ft.

Open to great room below

Br 4
12-7x12-0

Plant shelf above

Dn. Hall

Br 2
11-8x10-4

Balcony

open to entry below

Br 3
12-6x12-0

porch below

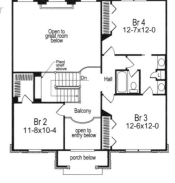

70'-0"

Patio

Patio

Breakfast
14-10x10-0

Great Room
20-6x15-8

sunken

Plant shelf above

MBr.
17-0x17-4
vaulted

Plant shelf above

Dn

Kitchen
14-10x10-6

D/W

46'-4"

Hall

Dn
Up

Pantry

Dining
14-10x12-4

Garage
21-4x20-4

Entry
2 story

W
D Laundry

Porch

© Copyright by designer/architect

First Floor
1,774 sq. ft.

Master Bath Features Curved Glass Block Wall

- 2,223 total square feet of living area
- Vaulted master bedroom opens to a private courtyard
- Master bath features a curved glass block wall around the tub and shower
- Vaulted family room combines with the breakfast room and kitchen to create a large casual living area
- Second floor includes secondary bedrooms and a possible loft/office
- 3 bedrooms, 2 1/2 baths, 2-car garage
- Basement foundation

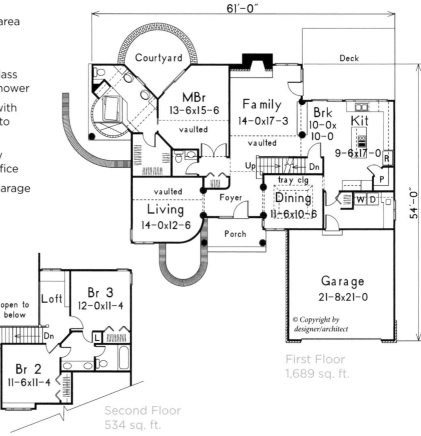

First Floor
1,689 sq. ft.

Second Floor
534 sq. ft.

Friendly Curb Appeal

- 2,908 total square feet of living area
- Energy efficient home with 2" x 6" exterior walls
- The open kitchen enjoys an angled center island with a double sink that overlooks the cheerful dining and sitting rooms
- Built-ins surround the fireplace in the cozy great room
- The owner's bedroom includes a sun-filled private sitting area and its own bath with a double-bowl vanity, amazing walk-in shower and a whirlpool tub
- 4 bedrooms, 2 1/2 baths, 3-car garage
- Walk-out basement foundation

Second Floor
1,533 sq. ft.

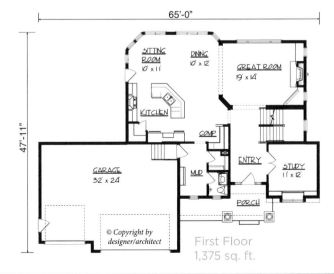

First Floor
1,375 sq. ft.

Stately Home Has Handsome Facade

- 2,816 total square feet of living area
- Enormous master bath has a beautiful corner whirlpool tub and an oversized walk-in closet
- Large center island in the kitchen is angled for interest and helps combine the space with the breakfast room
- Lots of windows brighten the great room
- Bonus room on the second floor has an additional 325 square feet of living area
- 3 bedrooms, 2 full baths, 2 half baths, 3-car side entry garage
- Walk-out basement foundation

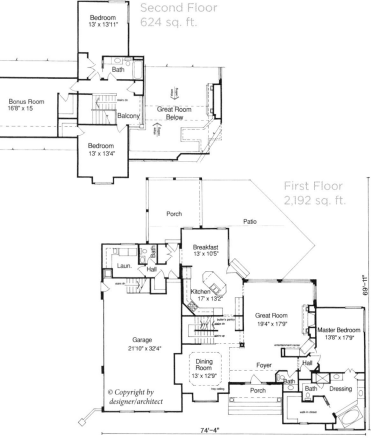

Second Floor
624 sq. ft.

Bedroom
13' x 13'11"

Bath

Bonus Room
16'8" x 15

Balcony

Great Room
Below

Bedroom
13' x 13'4"

First Floor
2,192 sq. ft.

Porch

Patio

Bath

Breakfast
13' x 10'5"

Laun.

Hall

Kitchen
17' x 13'2"

Great Room
19'4" x 17'9"

Master Bedroom
13'8" x 17'9"

Garage
21'10" x 32'4"

butler's pantry

entertainment center

Dining
Room
13' x 12'9"

Foyer

Hall

© Copyright by
designer/architect

Bath

Porch

Bath

Dressing

walk-in closet

74'-4"

69'-11"

Stunning Second Floor Balcony

- 2,843 total square feet of living area
- Step inside to view the elegant formal living and dining rooms flanking the foyer
- The massive great room is excellent for parties and large gatherings
- The master bedroom and hearth/breakfast room enjoy direct access onto the rear lanai
- The bonus area on the second floor has an additional 215 square feet of living area
- 4 bedrooms, 2 1/2 baths, 2-car side entry garage
- Slab or crawl space foundation, please specify when ordering

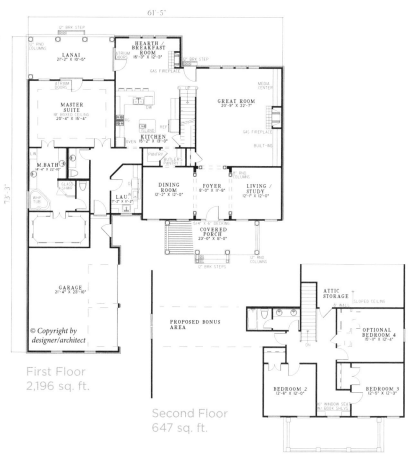

First Floor
2,196 sq. ft.

Second Floor
647 sq. ft.

Traditional Styling At Its Best

- 2,358 total square feet of living area
- The U-shaped kitchen provides an ideal layout; adjoining breakfast room allows for casual dining
- Formal dining and living rooms have attractive floor-to-ceiling windows
- Master bedroom includes a deluxe bath
- 4 bedrooms, 2 1/2 baths, 2-car garage
- Basement foundation, drawings also include crawl space and slab foundations

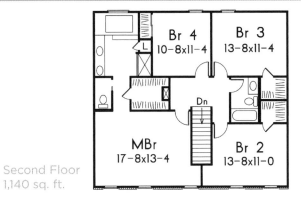

Br 4
10-8x11-4

Br 3
13-8x11-4

Dn

MBr
17-8x13-4

Br 2
13-8x11-0

Second Floor
1,140 sq. ft.

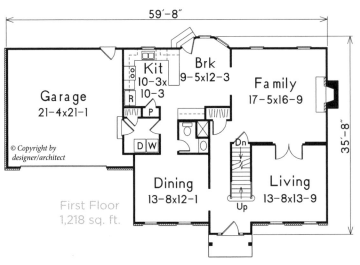

59'-8"

Garage
21-4x21-1

Kit
10-3x
10-3

Brk
9-5x12-3

Family
17-5x16-9

R

P

D W

Dn

35'-8"

© Copyright by
designer/architect

Dining
13-8x12-1

Up

Living
13-8x13-9

First Floor
1,218 sq. ft.

Timeless Value

- 3,445 total square feet of living area

- The flow of the first floor enhances the enjoyment of entertaining guests in the formal living and dining rooms, while the kitchen, hearth room and breakfast area combine for a comfortable casual atmosphere

- The second floor bayed master bedroom enjoys the warmth of a fireplace, walk-in closet and spacious dressing area

- The screened-in porch connects to the bayed breakfast area and an outdoor deck with eye-catching gazebo

- 4 bedrooms, 3 1/2 baths, 3-car side entry garage

- Walk-out basement foundation, drawings also include crawl space foundation

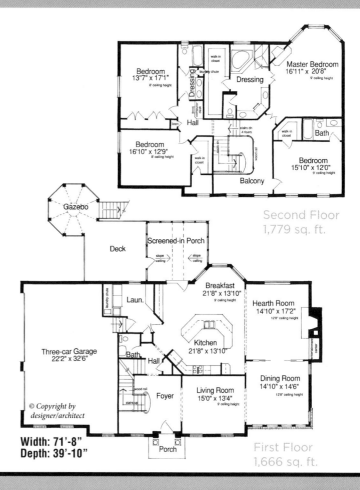

Second Floor
1,779 sq. ft.

First Floor
1,666 sq. ft.

Width: 71'-8"
Depth: 39'-10"

Handsome Traditional With Gabled Entrance

- 2,529 total square feet of living area

- Distinguished appearance enhances this home's classic interior arrangement

- A private bath with garden tub, walk-in closet and coffered ceiling enhance the master bedroom suite

- Bonus room over the garage, which is included in the square footage, has direct access from the attic and the second floor hall

- 4 bedrooms, 2 1/2 baths, 2-car garage

- Basement foundation

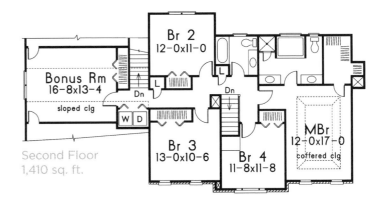

Br 2
12-0x11-0

Bonus Rm
16-8x13-4

sloped clg

Dn

W D

Br 3
13-0x10-6

Br 4
11-8x11-8

Dn

MBr
12-0x17-0
coffered clg

Second Floor
1,410 sq. ft.

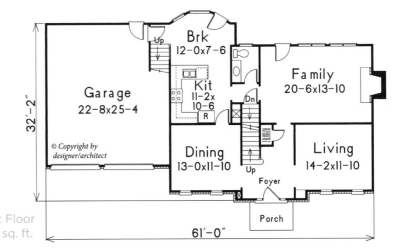

Brk
12-0x7-6

Up

Family
20-6x13-10

Garage
22-8x25-4

Kit
11-2x
10-6

R

Dn

© Copyright by
designer/architect

32-2"

Dining
13-0x11-10

Living
14-2x11-10

Up

Foyer

Porch

First Floor
1,119 sq. ft.

61'-0"

LOWE'S
LEGACY
SERIES

Exquisite Craftsman Style

- 2,470 total square feet of living area

- An extended counter in the kitchen has enough dining space for four people to gather around and enjoy a meal

- A media center is designed next to the fireplace in the cozy great room

- Rustic shutters and shingle siding add a great custom feel to the exterior of this home

- The bonus room above the garage offers an additional 389 square feet of future living area

- 4 bedrooms, 2 1/2 baths, 2-car garage

- Slab or crawl space foundation, please specify when ordering

Second Floor
875 sq. ft.

First Floor
1,595 sq. ft.

An Impressive Showplace

- 4,328 total square feet of living area

- The extra-large gourmet kitchen and breakfast room offer a spacious area for chores and family gatherings, while providing a striking view through the great room to the fireplace wall

- For convenience, a butler's pantry is located in the hall leading to the dining room

- An extravagant master bedroom and library round out the first floor

- The lavish lower level includes a media room, billiard room, exercise room and two bedrooms

- 3 bedrooms, 3 1/2 baths, 3-car side entry garage

- Walk-out basement foundation

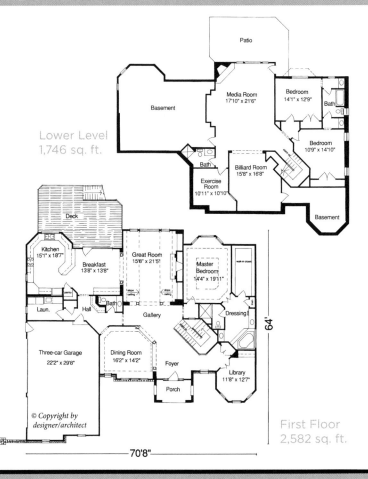

To Order See Page 288 or Call Toll-Free 1-877-379-3420

Varied Exterior Finishes Enrich Facade

- 2,696 total square feet of living area

- Magnificent master bedroom features a private covered porch and luxurious bath

- Second floor game room includes balcony access and an adjacent loft

- Well-planned kitchen includes a walk-in pantry, island cooktop and nearby spacious breakfast room

- 4 bedrooms, 3 baths, 2-car side entry garage

- Slab foundation, drawings also include crawl space foundation

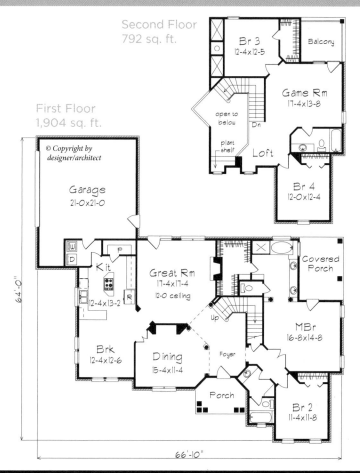

A Cozy Welcoming Covered Porch

- 3,669 total square feet of living area

- Energy efficient home with 2" x 6" exterior walls

- Square columns line the first floor keeping the interior spaces open and airy between the great room, dinette and kitchen

- A glorious sunroom can be found through double doors off the dinette

- The second floor loft is an ideal spot for a home office or computer area

- 4 bedrooms, 3 1/2 baths, 3-car garage

- Walk-out basement foundation

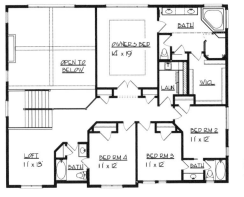

Second Floor
1,721 sq. ft.

66'-0"

50'-0"

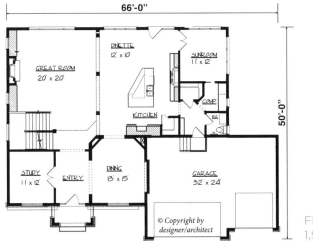

© Copyright by designer/architect

First Floor
1,948 sq. ft.

Stately Facade Features Impressive Front Balcony

- 2,411 total square feet of living area
- Elegant entrance features a two-story vaulted foyer
- Large family room is enhanced by a masonry fireplace and wet bar
- Master bath includes a walk-in closet, oversized tub and separate shower
- Second floor study could easily convert to a fourth bedroom
- 3 bedrooms, 2 1/2 baths, 2-car garage
- Basement foundation, drawings also include slab and crawl space foundations

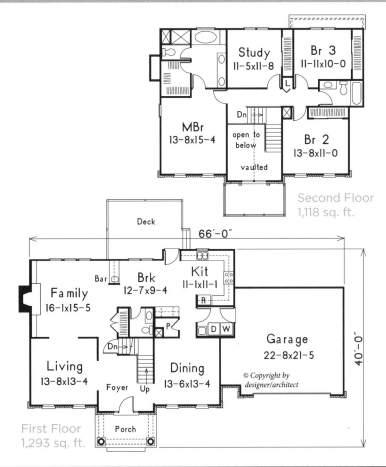

Lovely Arched Window Entry

- 2,653 total square feet of living area

- The sunken great room is a relaxing retreat with a grand fireplace

- The dining room opens onto the screened porch and the patio

- The kitchen features a walk-in pantry, expansive counterspace and an extra-large island

- 3 bedrooms, 2 1/2 baths, 2-car side entry garage

- Slab or crawl space foundation, please specify when ordering

Second Floor
1,246 sq. ft.

First Floor
1,407 sq. ft.

© Copyright by designer/architect

Luxury Home Abounds With Amenities

- 4,120 total square feet of living area
- Spacious rooms on both floors include two bedroom suites
- Elaborate master bedroom with a fireplace, double walk-in closets, deluxe tub and two private entrances
- Family room and kitchen form a large living area that includes a fireplace, corner window and vaulted ceiling
- Bonus room above the garage is included in the square footage
- 4 bedrooms, 3 full baths, 2 half baths, 2-car side entry garage
- Partial basement/crawl space foundation

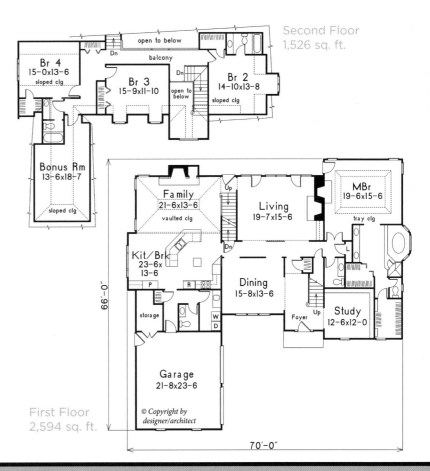

Second Floor
1,526 sq. ft.

Br 4
15-0x13-6
sloped clg

open to below

balcony

Dn

Br 3
15-9x11-10

open to below

Dn

Br 2
14-10x13-8
sloped clg

Bonus Rm
13-6x18-7

sloped clg

First Floor
2,594 sq. ft.

Family
21-6x13-6
vaulted clg

Up

Living
19-7x15-6

MBr
19-6x15-6
tray clg

Kit/Brk
23-6x
13-6

Dn

P

R

Dining
15-8x13-6

Foyer

Up

Study
12-6x12-0

storage

W
D

Garage
21-8x23-6

© Copyright by
designer/architect

66'-0"

70'-0"

Comfortable Living At Its Finest

- 3,013 total square feet of living area
- Oversized rooms throughout
- Kitchen features an island sink, large pantry and opens into the breakfast room with a sunroom feel
- Large family room with fireplace accesses the rear covered deck and front porch
- Master bedroom includes a large walk-in closet and private deluxe bath
- 4 bedrooms, 3 1/2 baths, 2-car side entry garage
- Basement foundation

Second Floor
1,554 sq. ft.

MBr
15-0x18-0
sloped clg

Br 4
10-0x11-0

Br 3
11-0x15-0

Dn

Br 2
14-0x16-0
raised clg

59'-4"

47'-4"

Garage
22-0x23-0

© Copyright by designer/architect

Brk
20-0x12-0

Covered Deck

Kit
18-0x14-0

Family
18-0x18-0

Dining
12-0x14-0

Dn

Up

Living
14-0x16-0

Porch

First Floor
1,459 sq. ft.

Stone Accents The Front Facade

- 3,176 total square feet of living area

- Energy efficient home with 2″ x 6″ exterior walls

- The lower level office provides the perfect amount of privacy and quiet when working from home

- An open and sunny porch extends off the dinette near the kitchen

- Both the laundry area and mud room create plenty of storage and organization for today's busy families

- 3 bedrooms, 2 1/2 baths, 3-car garage

- Walk-out basement foundation

First Floor
1,756 sq. ft.

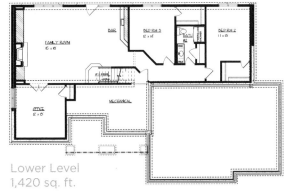

Lower Level
1,420 sq. ft.

Sweeping Elegant Front Colonnade

- 2,824 total square feet of living area
- 9' ceilings on the first floor
- Second floor bedrooms feature private dressing areas and share a bath
- Large great room includes a fireplace flanked by French doors leading to the rear patio
- Kitchen conveniently serves the formal dining room and breakfast area that features a large bay window
- 4 bedrooms, 3 baths, 2-car side entry garage
- Slab foundation, drawings also include crawl space foundation

Second Floor
704 sq. ft.

Br 2
12-10x15-5

Br 3
11-6x15-5

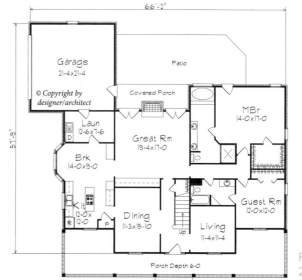

66'-2"

Garage
21-4x21-4

Patio

© Copyright by designer/architect

Covered Porch

51'-9"

Laun
12-6x7-6

MBr
14-0x17-0

Great Rm
19-4x17-0

Brk
14-0x9-0

Kit
12-0x

Guest Rm
12-0x12-0

Dining
11-3x15-10

Living
11-4x11-4

Porch Depth 6-0

First Floor
2,120 sq. ft.

Traditional Style With A Modern Twist

- 3,195 total square feet of living area
- Energy efficient home with 2″ x 6″ exterior walls
- Step into this stunning two-story and catch a view of the grand staircase flanked by the formal living and dining rooms
- A butler's pantry bridges the kitchen and the dining room for easy serving during dinner parties
- The master suite offers the option of having French doors leading into a sitting area or this area could be used as a fourth bedroom
- 4 bedrooms, 2 1/2 baths, 3-car garage
- Basement foundation

Second Floor
1,437 sq. ft.

First Floor
1,758 sq. ft.

Pleasing Covered Front Porch

- 3,117 total square feet of living area
- Energy efficient home with 2" x 6" exterior walls
- The cheerful kitchen has a double-bowl sink in the island and opens up nicely to the dinette area
- Spacious two-story great room offers a pleasant environment for gathering with family and friends
- The relaxing owner's bedroom offers a private bath with a generous closet, double-bowl vanity, amazing walk-in shower and a spa style tub to soak your cares away
- The bonus room on the second floor is included in the total square footage
- 3 bedrooms, 2 1/2 baths, 2-car garage
- Slab foundation

Second Floor
1,342 sq. ft.

First Floor
1,775 sq. ft.

Lowe's
LEGACY
SERIES

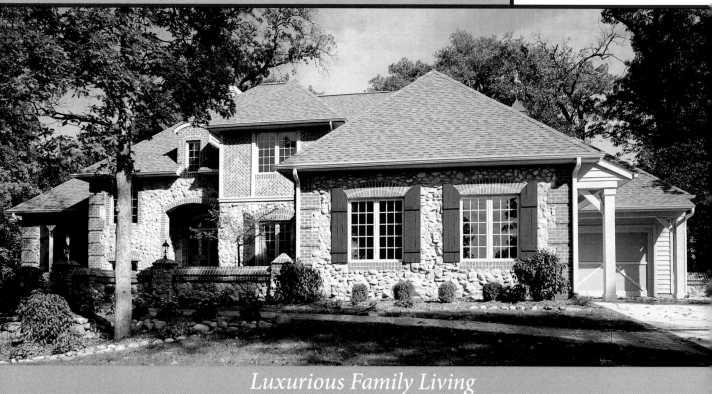

Luxurious Family Living

- 3,109 total square feet of living area

- Energy efficient home with 2" x 6" exterior walls

- A double-door entry elegantly leads into this home and back into the stunning great room

- Homeowners will enjoy the openness of the combined kitchen, nook and great room

- Relax in the master bedroom equipped with a pampering bath and walk-in closet

- 4 bedrooms, 2 1/2 baths, 2-car side entry garage, 1-car garage

- Basement foundation

Second Floor
885 sq. ft.

First Floor
2,224 sq. ft.

Stately Front Entrance With Style

- 2,614 total square feet of living area
- Grand two-story entry features a majestic palladian window, double French doors to the parlor and access to the powder room
- State-of-the-art kitchen has corner sink with two large archtop windows, island snack bar, menu desk and walk-in pantry
- Master bath is vaulted and offers a luxurious step-up tub, palladian window, built-in shelves and columns with plant shelf
- 4 bedrooms, 2 1/2 baths, 2-car garage
- Basement foundation

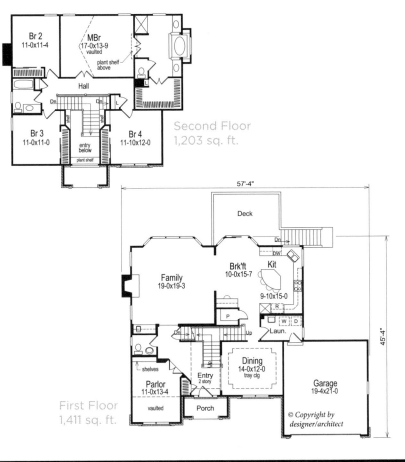

Second Floor
1,203 sq. ft.

First Floor
1,411 sq. ft.

© Copyright by designer/architect

Exquisite Details Throughout Home

- 3,421 total square feet of living area

- The gourmet kitchen with island and snack bar combines with the spacious breakfast and hearth rooms to create a warm and friendly atmosphere

- The luxurious master bedroom with sitting area and fireplace is complemented by a deluxe bath designed to pamper

- The optional lower level has an additional 1,777 square feet of living area and offers fun and excitement

- 3 bedrooms, 3 1/2 baths, 4-car side entry garage

- Walk-out basement foundation

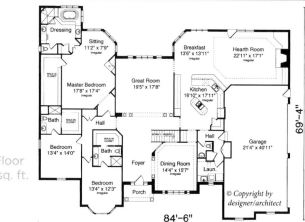

First Floor
3,421 sq. ft.

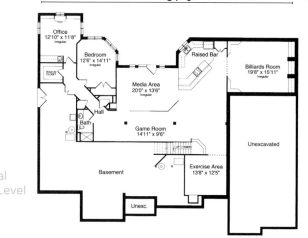

Optional
Lower Level

Pleasing Grand Front Porch

- 3,117 total square feet of living area
- Energy efficient home with 2″ x 6″ exterior walls
- The cheerful kitchen has a double-bowl sink in the island, a large pantry and opens up nicely to the dinette area
- The centralized fireplace is flanked by bookshelves in the great room
- The relaxing owner's bedroom offers a bath with a generous closet, double-bowl vanity, amazing walk-in shower and a spa style tub to soak your cares away
- 3 bedrooms, 2 1/2 baths, 2-car garage
- Slab foundation

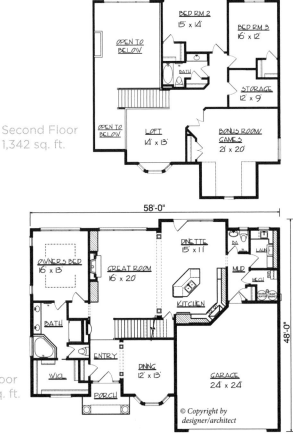

Second Floor
1,342 sq. ft.

First Floor
1,775 sq. ft.

Elegant Two-Story Exterior And Entry

- 2,846 total square feet of living area
- 9' ceilings on the first floor and 8' ceilings on the second floor
- Prominent double-bay windows and two-story foyer add brightness and space to both floors
- Master bedroom with double-door entry and coffered ceiling includes an elaborate bath with large tub, separate shower and individual walk-in closets
- Bonus room over the garage is included in the square footage
- 4 bedrooms, 2 1/2 baths, 2-car side entry garage
- Basement foundation, drawings also include slab and crawl space foundations

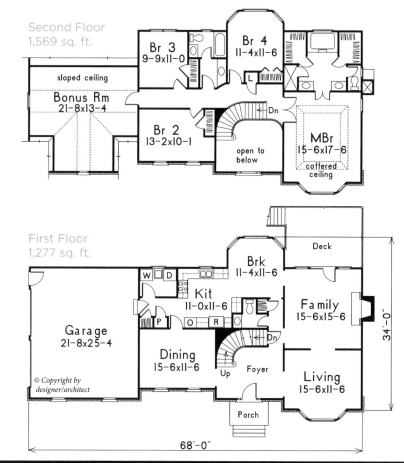

Second Floor
1,569 sq. ft.

Br 3
9-9x11-0

sloped ceiling

Bonus Rm
21-8x13-4

Br 4
11-4x11-6

Br 2
13-2x10-1

Dn

open to below

MBr
15-6x17-6

coffered ceiling

First Floor
1,277 sq. ft.

Deck

Brk
11-4x11-6

W D

Kit
11-0x11-6

Family
15-6x15-6

Garage
21-8x25-4

P

O R

Dn

Dining
15-6x11-6

Up   Foyer

Living
15-6x11-6

© Copyright by designer/architect

Porch

34'-0"

68'-0"

Rich Exterior With Eye-Catching Details

- 3,793 total square feet of living area

- The wide, welcoming foyer showcases columns at the entrance to the great room and dining room

- The spacious hearth room, breakfast area and kitchen combine to create a warm, inviting space perfect for cozy nights spent with the family

- The optional lower level includes space for a recreation room, bar, bedroom and bath and has an additional 1,588 square feet of living area

- 3 bedrooms, 2 1/2 baths, 3-car side entry garage

- Walk-out basement foundation

First Floor
3,793 sq. ft.

© Copyright by designer/architect

Width: 99'-8"
Depth: 68'-8"

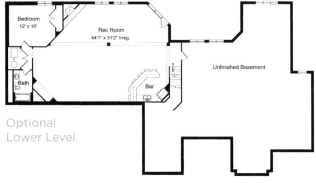

Optional
Lower Level

Grand-Scale Elegance

- 3,169 total square feet of living area
- Formal areas include an enormous entry with handcrafted stairway and powder room, French doors to the living room and an open dining area with tray ceiling
- Informal areas consist of a large family room with a bay window, fireplace, walk-in wet bar and kitchen open to the breakfast room
- Stylish master bedroom is located on the second floor for privacy
- Bedroom #3 includes a private study
- 4 bedrooms, 2 1/2 baths, 3-car side entry garage
- Basement foundation

Br 2
14-0x12-0

MBr
18-6x15-4
vaulted

Hall

plant shelf

Second Floor
1,490 sq. ft.

Br 3
14-0x12-8

Br 4
12-10x14-0

Study
8-0x9-10

55'-8"

Patio

Family
18-9x17-4

Wet Bar

Brk'ft
12-0x14-8

Kitchen
13-8x12-8

Pantry

Laundry

Dining
12-9x14-0
tray clg

Living
12-4x15-8

Entry

Garage
20-4x29-4

Porch

First Floor
1,679 sq. ft.

vaulted

51'-8"

© Copyright by designer/architect

Elegant Craftsman Details

- 2,393 total square feet of living area
- The dinette extends off the kitchen and has a large box-bay window for added sunlight
- A cozy fireplace warms the interior of the great room perfectly
- Right off the entry is a pleasing study perfect for a home office
- 3 bedrooms, 2 1/2 baths, 3-car garage
- Basement foundation

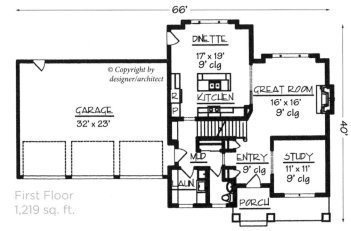

Second Floor
1,174 sq. ft.

BED RM
11' x 12'

BATH

FUTURE AREA
32' x 14'

OWNER'S SUITE
16' x 15'
9'-6" tray clg

BED RM
13' x 11'

W.I.C.

BATH

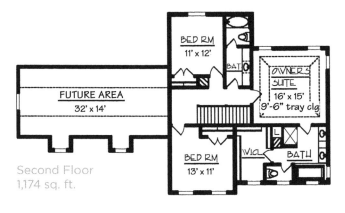

First Floor
1,219 sq. ft.

66'

40'

DINETTE
17' x 19'
9' clg

© Copyright by
designer/architect

KITCHEN

GREAT ROOM
16' x 16'
9' clg

GARAGE
32' x 23'

MUD

LAUN

ENTRY
9' clg

STUDY
11' x 11'
9' clg

PORCH

High-Style Modern Design

- 2,463 total square feet of living area
- Exciting angular design with diagonal stairway
- Living room features a vaulted ceiling, fireplace and convenient wet bar
- Generously sized family room features easy access to the kitchen
- Sunny bay window defines the breakfast area that accesses the deck
- 4 bedrooms, 2 1/2 baths, 2-car garage
- Basement foundation

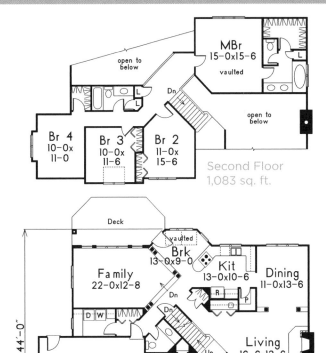

Second Floor
1,083 sq. ft.

First Floor
1,380 sq. ft.

A French Country Delight

- 3,816 total square feet of living area
- Beautifully designed master bedroom enjoys a lavish dressing area as well as access to the library
- Second floor computer loft is centrally located and includes plenty of counterspace
- The two-story great room has an impressive arched opening and a beautiful beamed ceiling
- The outdoor covered deck has a popular fireplace
- 4 bedrooms, 3 1/2 baths, 3-car side entry garage
- Basement foundation

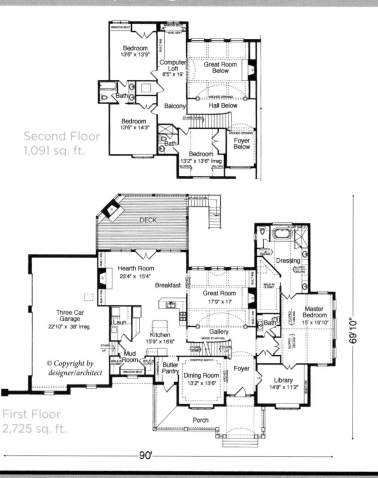

Second Floor
1,091 sq. ft.

First Floor
2,725 sq. ft.

Strong Craftsman Influence

- 3,242 total square feet of living area
- Energy efficient home with 2" x 6" exterior walls
- An enormous bayed dining room has an entire wall of built-ins perfect for storage and cookbooks
- Double doors off the entry lead to a secluded study perfect for a home office
- A large angled counter in the kitchen overlooks the bayed dining area and beyond to the great room
- 5 bedrooms, 2 1/2 baths, 3-car garage
- Basement foundation

First Floor 1,552 sq. ft.

Second Floor 1,690 sq. ft.

© Copyright by designer/architect

Superb Family Living

- 2,396 total square feet of living area

- A wall of glass partially separates the sun room from the breakfast room providing a cheerful atmosphere in both of these spaces

- The kitchen is filled with function including a large center island, a home office space, and baking and recycling centers

- A unique "swing suite" has direct access to a full bath and a convenient first floor location

- 4 bedrooms, 3 1/2 baths, 3-car garage

- Basement foundation

Second Floor
1,158 sq. ft.

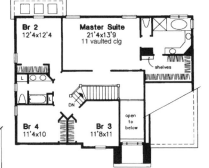

Br 2 12'4x12'4

Master Suite 21'4x13'9 11 vaulted clg

shelves

Br 4 11'4x10

Br 3 11'8x11

open to below

69'–8"

71'–4"

Deck

Sun Rm 12'5x11'2 skylit roof 9 clg

Family Room 21x14'3 9 clg entertainment

Swing Suite 11'5x10 9 clg

Brkfst 12'5x9 9 clg snack bar

Kitchen 19'6x17'6 9 clg

UP

DN

Dining 12'6x11 9 clg 18 clg

Living 12'6x15'9 18 vaulted clg

baking center

home office

recycle center

pantry

Ldry 7x14

bench

Three Car Garage 21x33

© Copyright by designer/architect

First Floor
1,238 sq. ft.

Impressive Country Design

- 2,193 total square feet of living area
- The airy great room is ideal for entertaining or gathering the family around the fireplace, while the open kitchen has a center island for easy meal preparation
- A formal dining room offers elegance when entertaining, while the nook is perfect for casual family dinners
- On the second floor, the master bedroom features a full bath and walk-in closet, while three additional bedrooms share a full bath
- 4 bedrooms, 2 1/2 baths, 3-car garage
- Basement foundation

Second Floor
1,080 sq. ft.

First Floor
1,113 sq. ft.

Bright Entrance Enlarges Foyer

- 2,336 total square feet of living area
- Two-story foyer with large second floor window creates a sunny, spacious entrance area
- Second floor play room is conveniently located near bedrooms as well as the laundry room
- Master bath has a vaulted ceiling and luxurious appointments
- Coffered ceiling enhances the master bedroom
- 4 bedrooms, 2 1/2 baths, 2-car garage
- Basement foundation

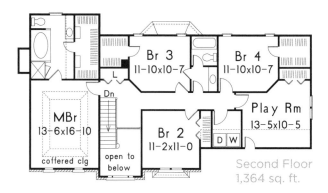

Br 3
11-10x10-7

Br 4
11-10x10-7

Play Rm
13-5x10-5

MBr
13-6x16-10
coffered clg

Br 2
11-2x11-0

Dn
open to below

Second Floor
1,364 sq. ft.

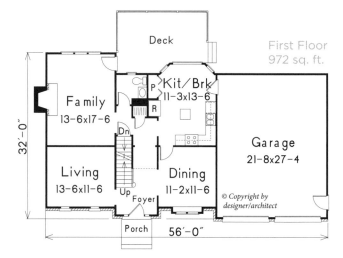

Deck

First Floor
972 sq. ft.

Kit/Brk
11-3x13-6

Family
13-6x17-6

Garage
21-8x27-4

Living
13-6x11-6

Dining
11-2x11-6

Foyer

Up

Dn

32'-0"

56'-0"

Porch

© Copyright by designer/architect

Quiet, Second Floor Bedrooms

- 2,356 total square feet of living area
- A stunning bay window adds curb appeal and offers a cheerful atmosphere in the formal living room
- The family room, sun room and dinette flow together with the kitchen for easy family living
- Convenience is created with the garage entrance having direct access to a half bath and mud room to contain any messes
- 4 bedrooms, 2 1/2 baths, 2-car garage
- Walk-out basement foundation

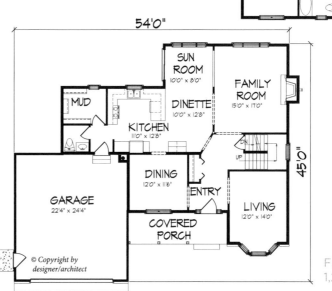

Second Floor
1,134 sq. ft.

MASTER SUITE
14'8" x 17'0"

BDRM 4
12'0" x 13'0"

W.I.C.

BDRM 3
11'6" x 11'0"

BDRM 2
12'4" x 14'0"

54'0"

SUN ROOM
10'0" x 8'0"

FAMILY ROOM
15'0" x 17'0"

MUD

DINETTE
10'0" x 12'8"

KITCHEN
11'0" x 12'8"

DINING
12'0" x 11'6"

ENTRY

45'0"

GARAGE
22'4" x 24'4"

COVERED PORCH

LIVING
12'0" x 14'0"

© Copyright by designer/architect

First Floor
1,222 sq. ft.

Stunning See-Through Fireplace

- 2,864 total square feet of living area
- The large, open kitchen is a chef's dream and features an angled serving bar that opens to the casual dinette and cozy hearth room
- Bay windows accentuate the first floor family room and the second floor master suite
- French doors off the entry access the quiet study that features handy built-ins for easy organization
- 4 bedrooms, 2 1/2 baths, 3-car garage
- Walk-out basement foundation

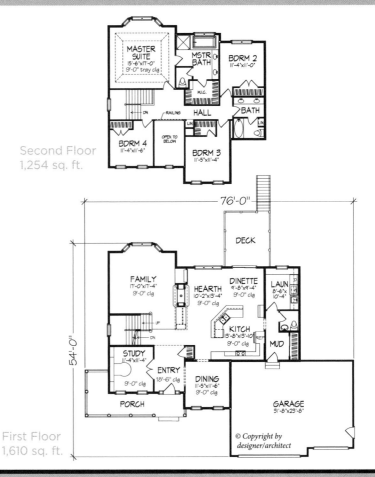

Second Floor
1,254 sq. ft.

First Floor
1,610 sq. ft.

Columns And Dormers Grace Stylish Exterior

- 3,216 total square feet of living area
- All bedrooms include private full baths
- Hearth room, breakfast area and kitchen create a large informal gathering area
- Oversized family room boasts a fireplace, wet bar and bay window
- Master bedroom has two walk-in closets and a luxurious bath
- 4 bedrooms, 4 1/2 baths, 3-car side entry garage
- Walk-out basement foundation

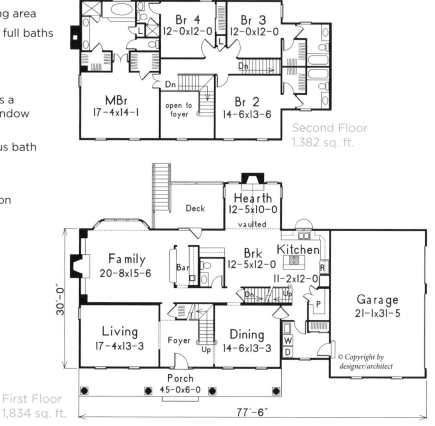

Br 4
12-0x12-0

Br 3
12-0x12-0

MBr
17-4x14-1

open to foyer

Br 2
14-6x13-6

Second Floor
1,382 sq. ft.

Deck

Hearth
12-5x10-0
vaulted

Family
20-8x15-6

Bar

Brk
12-5x12-0

Kitchen
11-2x12-0

30-0"

Living
17-4x13-3

Foyer

Dining
14-6x13-3

Garage
21-1x31-5

© Copyright by designer/architect

W D

Porch
45-0x6-0

77'-6"

First Floor
1,834 sq. ft.

European Luxury

- 2,889 total square feet of living area

- Stone, a striking turret and decorative roof lines accent this home and give it a European flair

- The luxurious first floor offers a massive great room, plush master suite, quiet office and access to the outdoor living porch furnished with a stone hearth fireplace

- The second floor consists of three bedrooms, a shared bath and handy computer center

- The second floor bonus room has an additional 378 square feet of living area

- 4 bedrooms, 2 1/2 baths, 2-car garage

- Crawl space or slab foundation, please specify when ordering

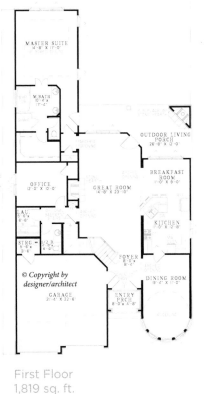

First Floor
1,819 sq. ft.

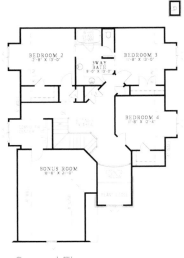

Second Floor
1,070 sq. ft.

Stately Colonial Entry

- 4,652 total square feet of living area
- A grand foyer introduces a formal dining room and library with beamed ceiling and built-ins
- Covered porches at the rear of the home offer splendid views
- A magnificent master bedroom has a 10' ceiling, a private sitting area and a luxurious dressing room with walk-in closet
- Secondary bedrooms have window seats, large closets and private bath access
- 4 bedrooms, 3 1/2 baths, 3-car side entry garage
- Walk-out basement foundation

Second Floor
1,238 sq. ft.

First Floor
3,414 sq. ft.

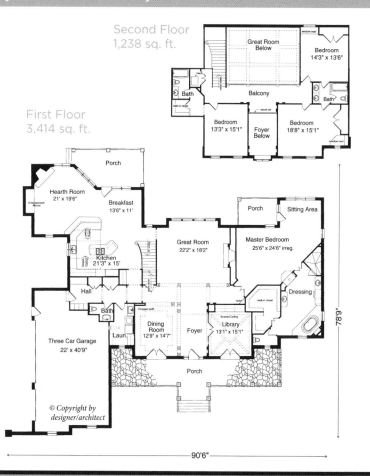

© Copyright by designer/architect

Two-Story Foyer Dramatizes Entrance

- 2,912 total square feet of living area
- Connected living and dining rooms each have full bay windows
- Elegant master bedroom boasts a sitting alcove, private deck and expansive coffered ceiling
- Impressive entrance and double-bay windows
- Bonus room, which is included in the square footage, can become a suite with its own private bath
- 3 bedrooms, 3 1/2 baths, 2-car garage
- Basement foundation

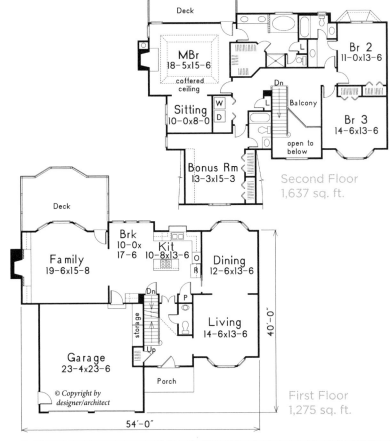

Second Floor
1,637 sq. ft.

First Floor
1,275 sq. ft.

© Copyright by designer/architect

Two-Story Foyer With Grand Curved Stairway

- 3,144 total square feet of living area
- 9' ceilings on the first floor
- Kitchen offers a large pantry, island cooktop and close proximity to the laundry and dining rooms
- Expansive family room includes a wet bar, fireplace and an attractive bay window
- 4 bedrooms, 3 1/2 baths, 3-car side entry garage
- Basement foundation

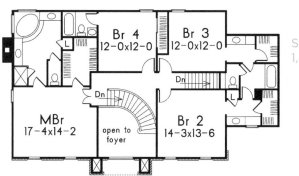

Second Floor
1,420 sq. ft.

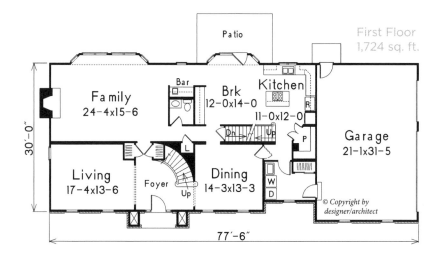

First Floor
1,724 sq. ft.

© Copyright by designer/architect

Luxury Home With Craftsman Charm

- 3,000 total square feet of living area
- Energy efficient home with 2″ x 6″ exterior walls
- A porch with sun room style extends off the spacious kitchen and dining area
- The lower level consists of a casual family room, a wet bar with surrounding game area and even a place for billiards
- The owner's suite is filled with extra amenities including a private pampering bath and a massive walk-in closet
- 3 bedrooms, 2 1/2 baths, 2-car garage, 1-car side entry garage
- Walk-out basement foundation

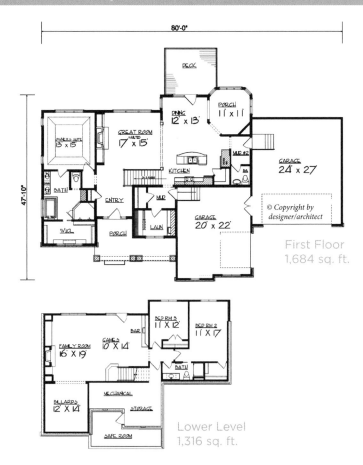

First Floor
1,684 sq. ft.

Lower Level
1,316 sq. ft.

Double Bay Windows Create Charming Formality

- 2,860 total square feet of living area
- Open two-story foyer
- Master bedroom suite, well isolated, includes impressive double-door entrances
- Convenient rear stairway
- Private access to hall bath from bedroom #3
- Bonus room above the garage is included in the square footage
- 3 bedrooms, 2 1/2 baths, 2-car garage
- Basement foundation

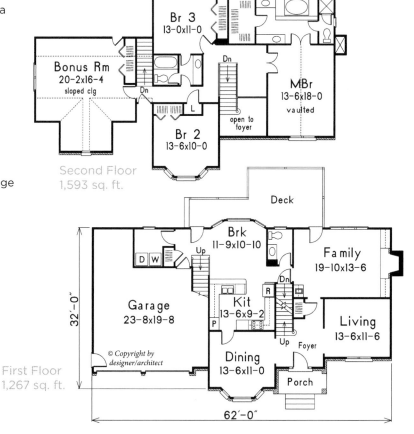

Second Floor
1,593 sq. ft.

First Floor
1,267 sq. ft.

Spectacular Floor Plan

- 4,160 total square feet of living area

- The cozy sitting area off the breakfast room offers a comfortable space for relaxation

- The master bedroom pleases with its private sitting alcove, entry to the rear deck and elegant dressing area

- The lower level is an inviting space to spend fun times with an exercise room, two additional bedrooms, a wet bar and space for a game table and media area

- 3 bedrooms, 2 1/2 baths, 2-car side entry garage

- Walk-out basement foundation

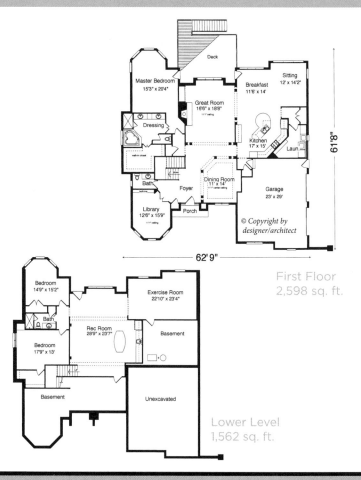

First Floor
2,598 sq. ft.

Lower Level
1,562 sq. ft.

To Order See Page 288 or Call Toll-Free 1-877-379-3420

LOWE'S LEGACY SERIES

Traditional With Attention To Detail

- 2,773 total square feet of living area
- Extensive use of bay and other large windows in the front and rear adds brightness and space
- Master bedroom suite features a double-door entrance, oversized walk-in closet and tray ceiling
- Rear stairway leads to both the bonus room, which is included in the square footage, and the laundry area on the second floor
- 4 bedrooms, 2 1/2 baths, 2-car side entry garage
- Basement foundation

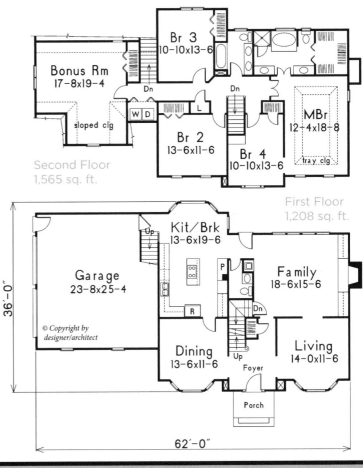

Second Floor 1,565 sq. ft.

Bonus Rm 17-8x19-4
sloped clg
Br 3 10-10x13-6
Br 2 13-6x11-6
Br 4 10-10x13-6
MBr 12-4x18-8
tray clg
W D
L

First Floor 1,208 sq. ft.

Garage 23-8x25-4
© Copyright by designer/architect
Kit/Brk 13-6x19-6
Family 18-6x15-6
Dining 13-6x11-6
Living 14-0x11-6
Foyer
Porch
Up
P
R
Dn

36'-0"
62'-0"

A Great Manor House, Spacious Inside And Out

- 3,368 total square feet of living area

- Sunken great room features a cathedral ceiling, wooden beams, skylights and a masonry fireplace

- Octagon-shaped breakfast room has domed ceiling with beams, large windows and door to patio

- Private master bedroom has a deluxe bath and dressing area

- Oversized walk-in closets and storage areas are located in each bedroom

- 4 bedrooms, 3 full baths, 2 half baths, 2-car side entry garage

- Basement foundation

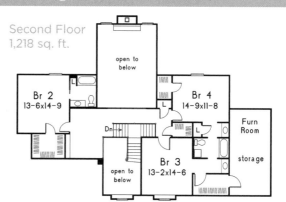

Second Floor
1,218 sq. ft.

open to below

Br 2
13-6x14-9

Br 4
14-9x11-8

Furn Room

storage

Dn

open to below

Br 3
13-2x14-6

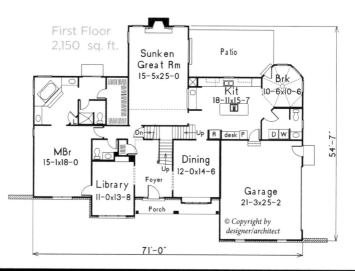

First Floor
2,150 sq. ft.

Sunken Great Rm
15-5x25-0

Patio

Brk
10-6x10-6

Kit
18-11x15-7

MBr
15-1x18-0

Up

Dn

R desk P

D W

Dining
12-0x14-6

Up

Library
11-0x13-8

Foyer

Garage
21-3x25-2

Porch

© Copyright by designer/architect

54'-7"

71'-0"

Lavish Two-Story With Double-Door Entry

- 3,730 total square feet of living area
- The spacious living room boasts a two-story ceiling
- The bayed morning room is full of warm light
- All three front rooms open to the outdoors through beautiful French doors
- 3 bedrooms, 2 1/2 baths, 2-car side entry garage
- Slab or crawl space foundation, please specify when ordering

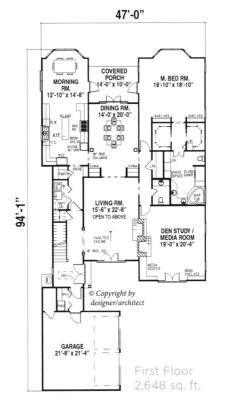

47'-0"

94'-1"

MORNING RM.
12'-10" x 14'-8"

COVERED PORCH
14'-0" x 10'-0"

M. BED RM.
18'-10" x 18'-10"

DINING RM.
14'-0" x 20'-0"

18" RND COLUMNS

LIVING RM.
15'-6" x 22'-8"
OPEN TO ABOVE

VAULTED CEILING

8" RND. COL.

DEN STUDY / MEDIA ROOM
19'-0" x 20'-4"

MEDIA CENTER

BOOK SHELVES

PANTRY

© Copyright by designer/architect

GARAGE
21'-8" x 21'-4"

First Floor
2,648 sq. ft.

BALCONY
14'-0" x 13'-0"

BED RM. 3
13'-10" x 13'-2"

BED RM. 2
23'-0" x 15'-8"

OPEN TO BELOW

OFF SEASON CEDAR CLOSET
14'-6" x 8'-0"

ATTIC STORAGE

Second Floor
1,082 sq. ft.

Pleasing Covered Front Porch

- 2,858 total square feet of living area
- Energy efficient home with 2″ x 6″ exterior walls
- A large island in the kitchen provides plenty of workspace when preparing meals as well as a double sink for added function
- The see-through fireplace separates the great room and the outdoor porch, warming the home inside and out
- The spacious and relaxing owner's suite offers an enormous closet, double-bowl vanity, amazing walk-in shower and a spa style tub
- 3 bedrooms, 3 1/2 baths, 3-car garage
- Walk-out basement foundation

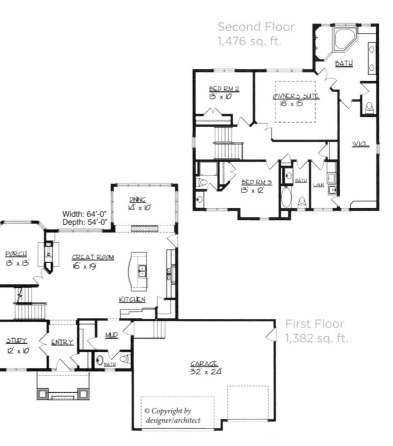

LOWE'S
LEGACY
SERIES

Stunning Ceiling Treatments

- 4,517 total square feet of living area

- A brick and stone exterior with a striking turret creates a strong facade for this delightful home

- An extra-large hearth room with gas fireplace connects to the breakfast area and kitchen for a comfortable family gathering place

- The spectacular lower level features a large recreation room, wine room, exercise room with sauna and two additional bedrooms

- 3 bedrooms, 2 full baths, 2 half baths, 2-car side entry garage, 1-car garage

- Walk-out basement foundation

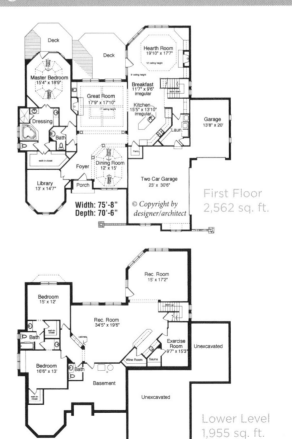

First Floor
2,562 sq. ft.

Lower Level
1,955 sq. ft.

Plan #542-072L-0980 • Price Code G

Extraordinary Country Home Has Luxurious Comforts

- 3,081 total square feet of living area

- The well-designed kitchen flows naturally into the dinette, that features access to the backyard and two columns

- The handsome family room is ideal for family gatherings with a cozy fireplace and a set of beautiful French doors

- The second floor has a lot to offer such as a huge bonus room for a kids' play area or adult game room

- 3 bedrooms, 2 1/2 baths, 3-car garage

- Basement foundation

Second Floor
1,723 sq. ft.

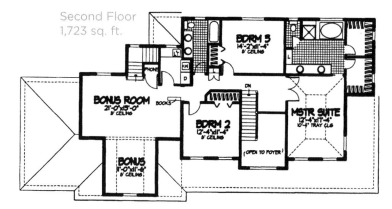

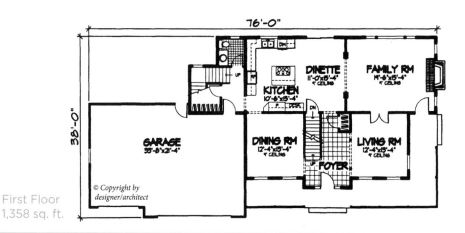

First Floor
1,358 sq. ft.

LOWE'S
LEGACY
SERIES

Gorgeous Georgian Home Design

- 2,653 total square feet of living area
- This amazing two-story Georgian style home is loaded with curb appeal
- The sunken family room has a comfortable atmosphere with a cozy fireplace
- The foyer is traditionally flanked by the formal living and dining rooms
- 4 bedrooms, 2 1/2 baths, 2-car side entry garage
- Walk-out basement foundation

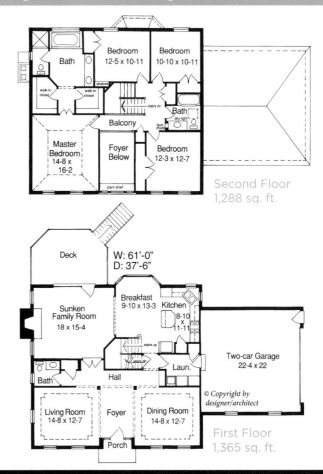

Second Floor
1,288 sq. ft.

First Floor
1,365 sq. ft.

Stylish Two-Story

- 3,688 total square feet of living area
- Formal and informal spaces throughout the home provide for various social events and comfortable family living
- A gourmet kitchen with breakfast bar and island serves the dining room and breakfast area with equal ease
- A secluded hall creates an orderly transition from the kitchen to the laundry room and garage
- A wonderful master bedroom is decorated by a stepped ceiling, crown molding, boxed window and lavish bath with a platform whirlpool tub
- 4 bedrooms, 3 1/2 baths, 3-car side entry garage
- Basement foundation

Second Floor
986 sq. ft.

Open to Great Room Below

Bath

Bedroom
17'4" x 11'1"

Hall

Bedroom
14'8" x 11'3"

Foyer Below

Bath

WALK-IN CLOSET

Bedroom
12'4" x 13'8"

First Floor
2,702 sq. ft.

Porch

Master Bedroom
20'3" x 16'

Great Room
18'6" x 17'10"

Breakfast
12'4" x 12'8"

Hearth Room
19'7" x 19'3"

Kitchen
13'1" x 15'6"

Hall

Laun.

Dressing

Library
11'8" x 14'

Foyer

Porch

Dining Room
13' x 14'

Three Car Garage
21'4" x 36'2"

64'11"

75'

© Copyright by designer/architect

To Order See Page 288 or Call Toll-Free 1-877-379-3420

Cozy Porches, Front And Back

- 2,672 total square feet of living area

- 9' ceilings on the first floor

- Combined kitchen and breakfast area

- Large family room is graced by a corner fireplace

- Convenient storage above garage

- Rear covered porch is adjacent to bedroom #2 and the family room

- Future room on the second floor has an additional 161 square feet of living area

- 4 bedrooms, 3 baths, 2-car rear entry garage

- Slab foundation, drawings also include crawl space foundation

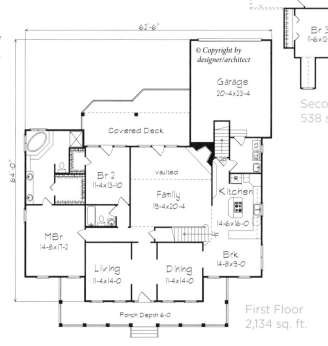

Second Floor
538 sq. ft.

First Floor
2,134 sq. ft.

Impressive Elegance In A Rambling Two-Story

- 3,116 total square feet of living area

- Arched mullioned windows provide balance across the impressive facade

- First floor master bedroom and bedroom #2 on the second floor have private baths and walk-in closets

- Vaulted ceiling and balcony add even more spaciousness

- Bonus room above the garage, which is included in the square footage, is available for future use

- 4 bedrooms, 3 1/2 baths, 2-car side entry garage

- Basement foundation

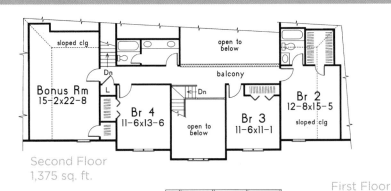

Second Floor
1,375 sq. ft.

First Floor
1,741 sq. ft.

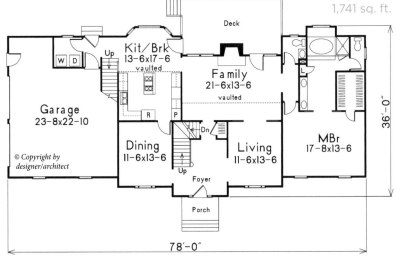

Early American Touches

- 2,376 total square feet of living area

- The incredible kitchen is quite appealing and includes a center island with raised seating as well as a built-in desk and generous pantry

- The wonderful family room has a handsome fireplace, three windows for brightness and optional French doors that lead to the grand living room

- The master suite offers homeowners a walk-in closet, a double-bowl vanity and a relaxing shower

- 4 bedrooms, 2 1/2 baths, 3-car side entry garage

- Basement foundation, drawings also include crawl space foundation

Second Floor
1,128 sq. ft.

First Floor
1,248 sq. ft.

LOWE'S LEGACY SERIES

Two-Story Offers Attractive Exterior

- 2,262 total square feet of living area
- Energy efficient home with 2" x 6" exterior walls
- Charming exterior features include a large front porch, two patios, a front balcony and double bay windows
- The den provides an impressive entry to the sunken family room
- Large master bedroom has a walk-in closet, dressing area and bath
- 3 bedrooms, 2 1/2 baths, 2-car rear entry garage
- Crawl space foundation, drawings also include basement and slab foundations

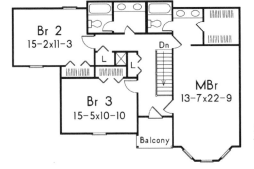

Br 2
15-2x11-3

Dn

Br 3
15-5x10-10

MBr
13-7x22-9

Balcony

Second Floor
1,135 sq. ft.

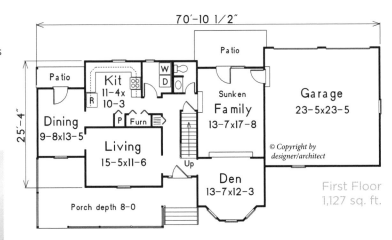

70'-10 1/2"

Patio

Patio

Kit
11-4x
10-3

W
D

Garage
23-5x23-5

25'-4"

Dining
9-8x13-5

P   Furn

Sunken
Family
13-7x17-8

© Copyright by
designer/architect

Living
15-5x11-6

Up

Den
13-7x12-3

First Floor
1,127 sq. ft.

Porch depth 8-0

LOWE'S
LEGACY
SERIES

Cheerful Dining Area

- 3,320 total square feet of living area
- Energy efficient home with 2" x 6" exterior walls
- The sunny octagon-shaped dining room has access to the rear deck
- The double-sided fireplace warms the great room and the hearth room providing a bold statement that homeowners will enjoy
- The lower level boasts a corner fireplace in the expansive family room and access to a large storage area, which is highly convenient
- 3 bedrooms, 2 1/2 baths, 3-car garage
- Walk-out basement foundation

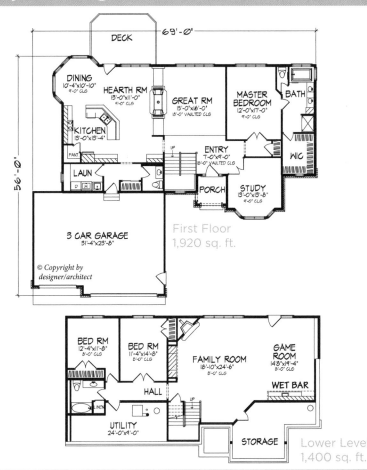

Classic Italian Design

- 5,143 total square feet of living area
- Energy efficient home with 2″ x 6″ exterior walls
- The first floor has an enormous amount of luxury including a grand foyer and library both with custom cabinetry and an impressive master bedroom with lavish dressing area and walk-in closet
- The second floor bedrooms all have walk-in closets and 9′ ceilings while enjoying the hall gallery
- The optional lower level offers an additional 1,351 square feet of living area and includes a sitting room with fireplace, media center, wine storage and exercise room
- 4 bedrooms, 3 1/2 baths, 3-car side entry garage
- Walk-out basement foundation

Second Floor
1,820 sq. ft.

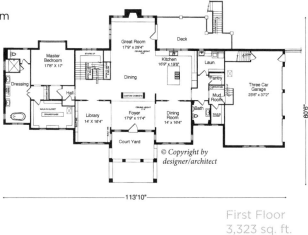

© Copyright by designer/architect

First Floor
3,323 sq. ft.

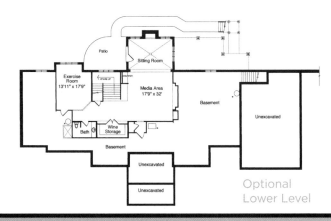

Optional
Lower Level

All Brick Traditional Design Exudes Elegance

- 4,020 total square feet of living area
- The large country kitchen is sure to be a gathering spot with its spacious feel and organized design
- An entire wall of windows in the living room overlooks an angled deck
- The lower level family room provides a large wet bar perfect for entertaining
- 3 bedrooms, 3 baths, 3-car side entry garage
- Walk-out basement foundation

First Floor
2,572 sq. ft.

Lower Level
1,448 sq. ft.

Many Exciting Features

- 2,738 total square feet of living area

- An open entrance offers a spectacular view of the windowed rear wall and fireplace in the great room

- The kitchen, breakfast and hearth rooms combine to offer an open and comfortable gathering place

- The master bedroom is topped with an 11' ceiling and features a sitting alcove and deluxe bath

- 4 bedrooms, 3 1/2 baths, 2-car side entry garage

- Basement foundation

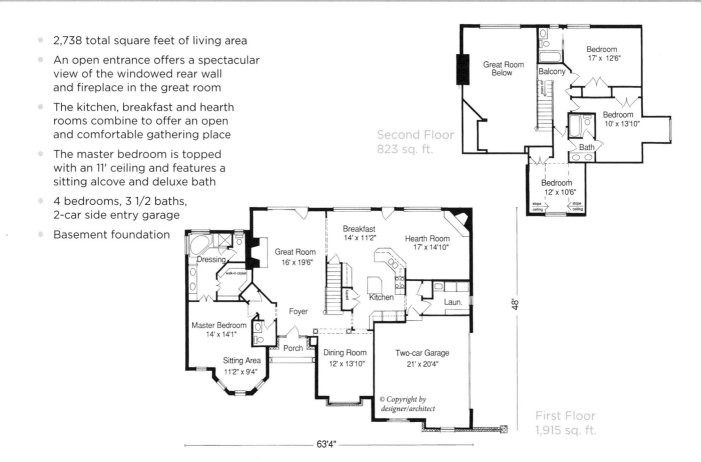

Second Floor
823 sq. ft.

First Floor
1,915 sq. ft.

© Copyright by designer/architect

A Traditional Home For Lots Of Living

- 2,940 total square feet of living area
- Two sets of twin dormers add outdoor charm while lighting the indoors
- Massive central foyer leads into the sunken living room below and has access to the second floor attic
- Private master bedroom is complete with a bath featuring a luxurious corner tub and large walk-in closet
- A novel bridge provides a view of the living room below and access to second floor attic
- 4 bedrooms, 3 baths, 2-car side entry garage
- Walk-out basement foundation

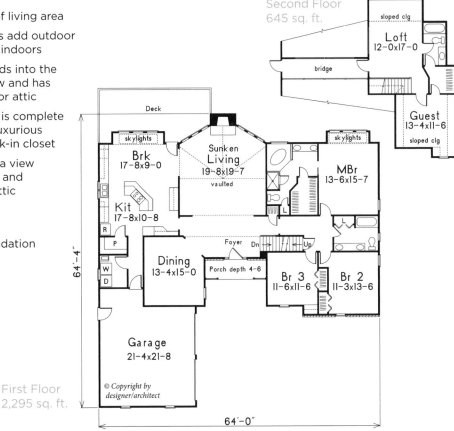

A Substantial Brick Home

- 3,015 total square feet of living area
- The octagon-shaped dinette is ideal for enjoying a morning cup of coffee while the efficient kitchen has a stylish snack bar for casual dining
- The handsome family room has three beautiful window accents, a cozy fireplace and an open design that flows nicely into the kitchen
- The second floor is composed of a multi-purpose room, two bedrooms, a master suite and a useful laundry room
- 3 bedrooms, 2 1/2 baths, 3-car garage
- Basement foundation

Second Floor
1,648 sq. ft.

First Floor
1,367 sq. ft.

Balcony Provides Dramatic View Below To Great Room

- 2,157 total square feet of living area

- Varied ceiling treatments, spacious rooms and lots of windows combine to set this home apart from the ordinary

- A spacious kitchen has a peninsula and walk-in pantry

- The master bedroom has every luxury imagined

- 4 bedrooms, 2 1/2 baths, 2-car side entry garage

- Walk-out basement foundation

Second Floor
646 sq. ft.

Bedroom
11' x 10'4"

Bedroom
10'10' x 11'3"

Great Room
Below

Balcony

Bath

Foyer
Below

Bedroom
11'2" x 12'11"

plant shelf

First Floor
1,511 sq. ft.

Deck

Breakfast
11' x 9'

Hall

Kitchen
13'2" x 12'7"

Great Room
16'6" x 17'2"

Master
Bedroom
14' x 17'10"

Laun.

slope ceiling   slope ceiling

pantry   wood rail

walk-in closet

Two-car Garage
23'9" x 20'0"

Dining Room
11'2" x 15'4"

Foyer

Bath

© Copyright by
designer/architect

54'8"

Georgian Style Inspiration

- 2,416 total square feet of living area
- The large grand entry invites guests in and steps lead to the grand family room
- Tray ceilings adorn both the master suite and luxurious bath creating a feeling of elegance
- A built-in TV cabinet is located next to the cozy fireplace in the family room
- Bonus room on the second floor has an additional 243 square feet of living area
- 3 bedrooms, 2 1/2 baths, 3-car garage
- Basement foundation

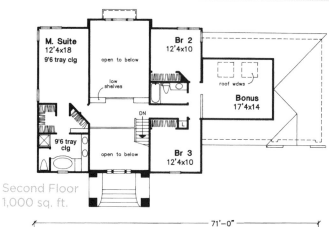

Second Floor
1,000 sq. ft.

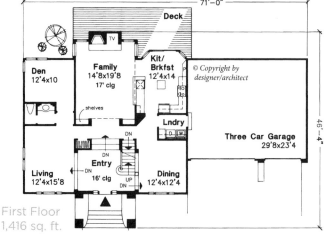

First Floor
1,416 sq. ft.

Exterior Accents Complement Front Facade

- 2,282 total square feet of living area
- Balcony and two-story foyer add spaciousness to this plan
- First floor master bedroom has a corner tub in the large private bath
- Out-of-the-way kitchen is open to the full-windowed breakfast room
- 4 bedrooms, 2 1/2 baths, 2-car drive under side entry garage
- Basement foundation

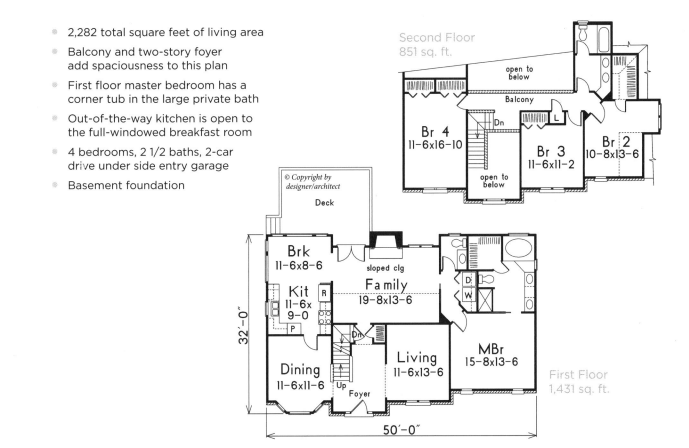

Second Floor
851 sq. ft.

Br 4
11-6x16-10

Br 3
11-6x11-2

Br 2
10-8x13-6

Balcony

open to below

open to below

© Copyright by designer/architect

Deck

Brk
11-6x8-6

sloped clg

Family
19-8x13-6

Kit
11-6x
9-0

Dining
11-6x11-6

Living
11-6x13-6

MBr
15-8x13-6

Foyer

Up

Dn

32'-0"

50'-0"

First Floor
1,431 sq. ft.

Unique Architectural Details

- 4,220 total square feet of living area
- This two-story home is designed perfectly to suit the needs of a busy family featuring an "US" room, activity area, multi-purpose room and even a kid's study
- Spacious garden spaces surround this home creating pleasant outdoor living areas perfect for relaxing
- Interesting architectural details exist on the second floor with curved glass block walls around the staircase and curved built-in desks in both the office and kid's study
- 3 bedrooms, 4 1/2 baths, 2-car garage
- Basement foundation

Second Floor
1,452 sq. ft.

First Floor
2,768 sq. ft.

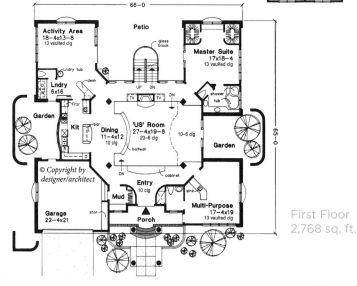

To Order See Page 288 or Call Toll-Free 1-877-379-3420

LOWE'S **LEGACY** SERIES

Superb Craftsman Style Luxury

- 3,159 total square feet of living area
- Energy efficient home with 2″ x 6″ exterior walls
- An impressive master bath includes a spacious walk-in closet and built-in tub perfect for relaxing
- The kitchen is open and efficient with a large, curved island for easy dining
- Double-door entry to the study reveals a beautiful built-in work area and lovely windows for added light
- 4 bedrooms, 3 1/2 baths, 3-car garage
- Basement foundation

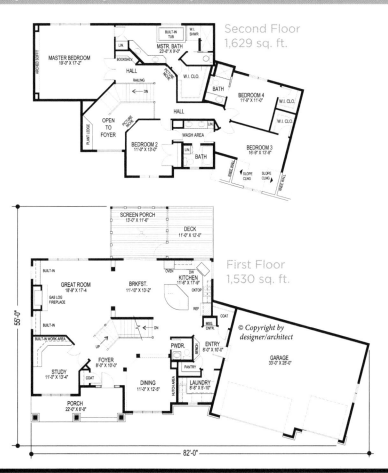

Second Floor 1,629 sq. ft.

First Floor 1,530 sq. ft.

© Copyright by designer/architect

Craftsman Home

- 3,770 total square feet of living area
- Energy efficient home with 2″ x 6″ exterior walls
- Spacious kitchen has a center island with double sink and snack bar
- The sitting room near the kitchen features a corner fireplace and has access to the rear deck and lovely vaulted screen porch
- The luxurious, second floor master bedroom has abundant storage space and a plush bath
- The bonus room above the garage has an additional 256 square feet of living space
- 4 bedrooms, 3 1/2 baths, 3-car garage
- Basement foundation

Second Floor
1,952 sq. ft.

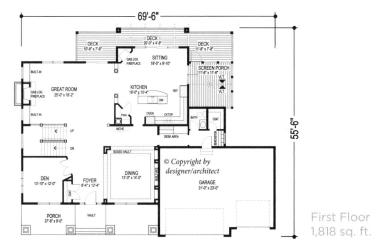

© Copyright by designer/architect

First Floor
1,818 sq. ft.

Beautiful One-Level Home

- 2,959 total square feet of living area

- A beamed ceiling tops the great room and a fireplace and built-ins decorate one wall

- A breakfast area, sitting area and stylish kitchen create a family center perfect for casual gatherings

- A library with built-in shelving and angled walls provides an area dedicated for organized work at home

- 3 bedrooms, 2 1/2 baths, 3-car side entry garage

- Walk-out basement foundation

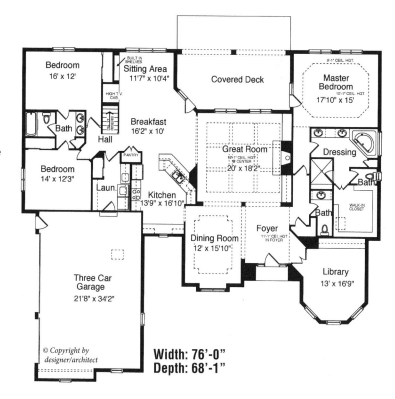

Width: 76'-0"
Depth: 68'-1"

Relaxing Hearth Room

- 2,606 total square feet of living area

- A corner fireplace in the great room warms the area and the adjoining dining room

- French doors lead into the study/bedroom #4 which features a bay window and has access to a private patio

- The garage includes a convenient storage space

- The optional second floor has an additional 751 square feet of living space

- 4 bedrooms, 2 1/2 baths, 2-car side entry garage

- Slab, basement, crawl space or walk-out basement foundation, please specify when ordering

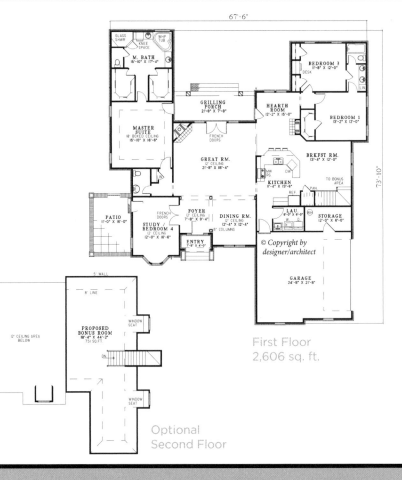

First Floor
2,606 sq. ft.

Optional
Second Floor

Lowe's LEGACY SERIES

Private Guest Quarters On Lower Level

- 3,059 total square feet of living area
- Covered porches surround the exterior of this home
- The laundry area is adjacent to the hobby area that is connected to the garage
- Bedroom #2 has a bayed sitting area making it also ideal as a study
- 4 bedrooms, 4 baths, 2-car side entry garage
- Crawl space, slab, or basement foundation, please specify when ordering

First Floor
2,650 sq. ft.

Lower Level
409 sq. ft.

Stunning Home With Lots Of Space For Family

- 2,824 total square feet of living area

- Kitchen with optional island is open to the breakfast nook and hearth room

- Great room has fireplace, 8″ columns and access to a rear grilling porch

- Master bath has large walk-in closet, split vanities, corner whirlpool bath and a separate shower

- Bonus room on second floor has an additional 410 square feet of living area

- 4 bedrooms, 3 baths, 2-car side entry garage

- Basement foundation

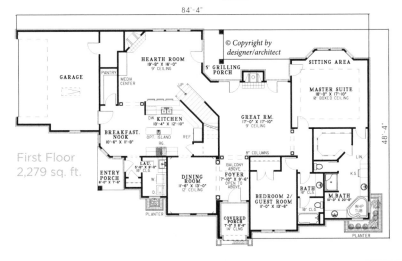

Second Floor
545 sq. ft.

First Floor
2,279 sq. ft.

Stately Home Captures Continental Flavor

- 3,017 total square feet of living area
- Convenient L-shape entry brings formality to this 1 1/2 story plan
- The loft features a palladian window overlooking the family room
- First floor bedrooms each have a private full bath
- Master bedroom includes a bay window and corner tub in the bath
- Bonus room above the garage is included in the square footage
- 4 bedrooms, 3 1/2 baths, 2-car side entry garage
- Partial basement/crawl space foundation

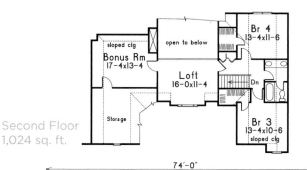

Second Floor
1,024 sq. ft.

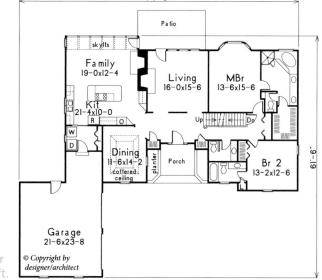

First Floor
1,993 sq. ft.

© Copyright by designer/architect

Stylish Ranch Living With Great Amenities

- 3,465 total square feet of living area
- Energy efficient home with 2″ x 6″ exterior walls
- The lower level features a combined family and games space with a massive wet bar including plenty of counterspace for great entertaining
- Open and airy, the great room is vaulted and topped with a charming beamed ceiling
- A spa-style tub is the highlight of the master bath
- 3 bedrooms, 2 1/2 baths, 3-car garage
- Walk-out basement foundation

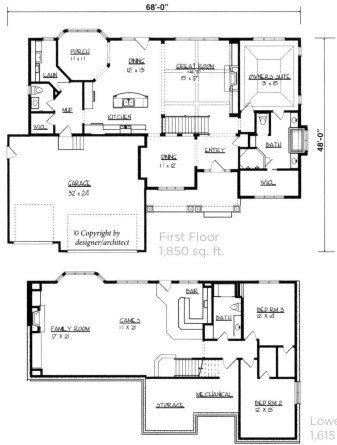

First Floor
1,850 sq. ft.

Lower Level
1,615 sq. ft.

Enchanting Outdoor Living Area

- 2,611 total square feet of living area
- Enter the stunning foyer to find a brilliant great room with a gorgeous fireplace and a beamed ceiling adding a rustic touch
- A full wall of windows enhances the dining room with sunlight
- A large game room over the garage is the perfect casual escape and offers an additional 424 square feet of living area
- 3 bedrooms, 2 1/2 baths, 3-car side entry garage
- Crawl space, basement, slab or walk-out basement foundation, please specify when ordering

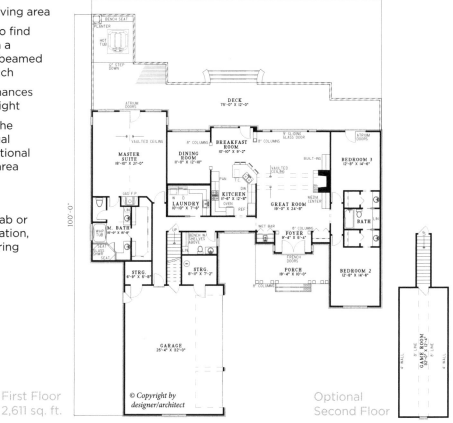

First Floor
2,611 sq. ft.

© Copyright by
designer/architect

Optional
Second Floor

Large Bayed Breakfast Area

- 2,603 total square feet of living area

- The vaulted great room includes a media center, fireplace and access to the covered grilling porch

- A convenient storage area is located in the garage

- The second floor bedrooms share a unique computer center

- The bonus room on the second floor has an additional 410 square feet of living space

- 4 bedrooms, 3 baths, 2-car side entry garage

- Slab or crawl space foundation, please specify when ordering

Second Floor
790 sq. ft.

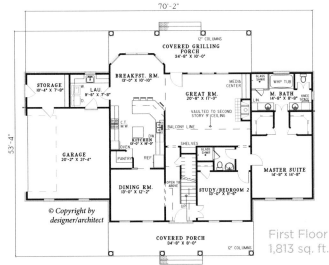

First Floor
1,813 sq. ft.

Gorgeous Brick Exterior

- 2,534 total square feet of living area

- The private master suite enjoys a 10' box ceiling and a deluxe bath with two vanities and walk-in closets

- A large laundry room is conveniently located adjacent to the garage entrance and the kitchen

- Elegant French doors lead into the study

- 3 bedrooms, 2 baths, 3-car side entry garage

- Slab or crawl space foundation, please specify when ordering

See-Through Fireplace Warms Living Areas

- 3,108 total square feet of living area
- The two-story great room features French doors to the rear deck
- The kitchen and breakfast room combine and include a cooktop island, walk-in pantry and TV cabinet
- Second floor bonus rooms provide an additional 485 square feet of living space
- 3 bedrooms, 2 1/2 baths, 3-car side entry garage
- Slab or crawl space foundation, please specify when ordering

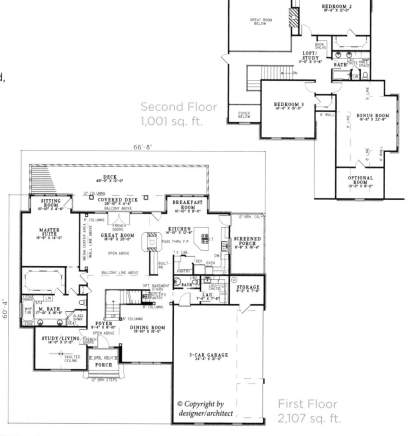

Second Floor
1,001 sq. ft.

First Floor
2,107 sq. ft.

© Copyright by designer/architect

Sprawling Family Farmhouse

- 2,972 total square feet of living area
- Extra storage is available beyond bedroom #2 on the second floor
- The angled staircase in the entry adds interest
- Charming screened porch is accessible from the breakfast area
- Bonus room above the garage has an additional 396 square feet of living area
- 4 bedrooms, 3 1/2 baths, 3-car side entry garage
- Walk-out basement foundation, drawings also include crawl space and slab foundations

Second Floor
986 sq. ft.

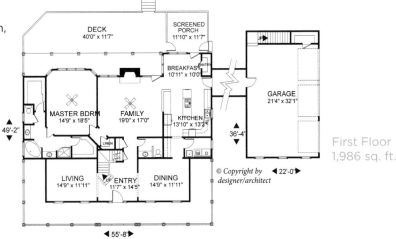

First Floor
1,986 sq. ft.

© Copyright by designer/architect

Stunning Ranch Filled With Light

- 3,183 total square feet of living area

- A wonderful open kitchen, breakfast and hearth room arrangement is sure to be the family's favorite places to gather

- A distinctive master bath has a unique balance of style with a centered whirlpool tub and two vanities

- The formal living room is generous in size and exquisite in design featuring a vaulted ceiling and lovely atrium doors leading to the grilling porch

- 4 bedrooms, 2 1/2 baths, 3-car side entry garage

- Crawl space or slab foundation, please specify when ordering

Private Master Entry

- 2,777 total square feet of living area

- A warm and pleasant hearth room is also enjoyed by the bayed breakfast room

- A 10' deep covered porch in the front of the home creates outdoor living space for relaxing

- A second floor computer center is the ideal design for a mini office or student projects

- 4 bedrooms, 2 1/2 baths, 2-car side entry garage

- Slab or crawl space foundation, please specify when ordering

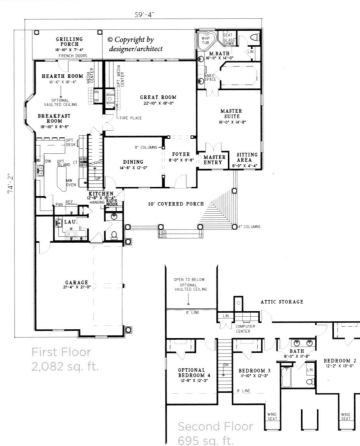

First Floor
2,082 sq. ft.

Second Floor
695 sq. ft.

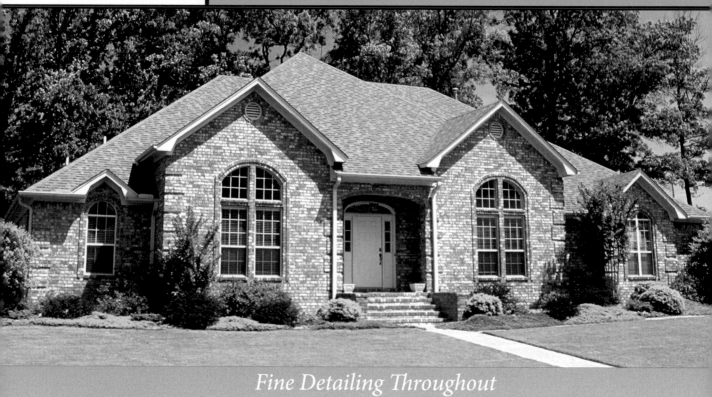

Fine Detailing Throughout

- 2,742 total square feet of living area

- The luxurious master suite includes a wall of built-ins along with a private entrance to the rear porch

- A fireplace nicely settled between built-ins punctuates the enormous great room

- The oversized laundry/hobby room offers an abundance of space for do-it-yourself home projects

- The optional second floor has an additional 352 square feet of living space

- 3 bedrooms, 2 1/2 baths, 2-car side entry garage

- Crawl space or slab foundation, please specify when ordering

Optional
Second Floor

First Floor
2,742 sq. ft.

© Copyright by
designer/architect

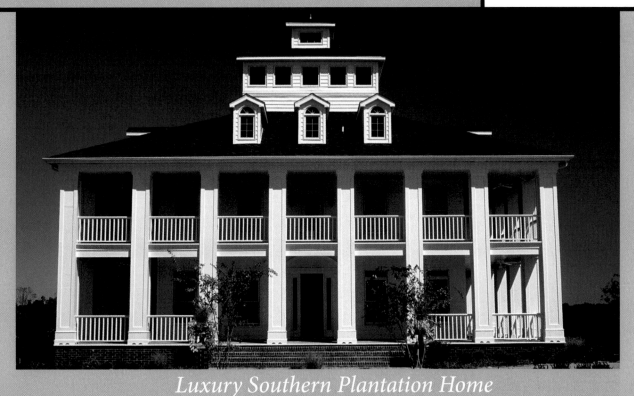

Luxury Southern Plantation Home

- 5,689 total square feet of living area

- Wrap-around porches with boxed columns welcome family and friends into this Southern-styled home

- Access all floors by the elevator or take the beautiful spiral staircase from the second floor up to the spacious hobby room

- Entertain with ease in the lower level game room that is complete with a kitchen area and outdoor access

- The optional third floor hobby room has an additional 1,744 square feet of living area

- 5 bedrooms, 4 1/2 baths, 3-car drive under side entry garage

- Walk-out basement foundation

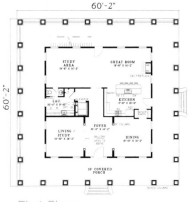

First Floor
1,600 sq. ft.

Second Floor
1,530 sq. ft.

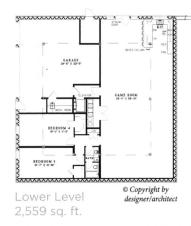

Lower Level
2,559 sq. ft.

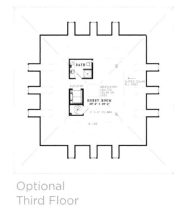

Optional
Third Floor

Striking Double-Arched Entry

- 3,494 total square feet of living area
- Majestic two-story foyer opens into the living and dining rooms, both framed by arched columns
- Balcony overlooks the large living area featuring French doors to a covered porch
- Luxurious master bedroom
- Convenient game room supports lots of activities
- 4 bedrooms, 3 1/2 baths, 3-car side entry garage
- Slab foundation, drawings also include crawl space foundation

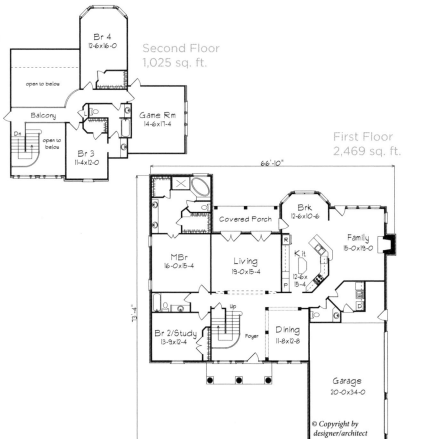

Second Floor
1,025 sq. ft.

Br 4
12-6x16-0

open to below

Balcony

Dn

open to below

Br 3
11-4x12-0

Game Rm
14-6x17-4

First Floor
2,469 sq. ft.

66'-10"

73'-4"

MBr
16-0x15-4

Covered Porch

Brk
12-6x10-6

Family
15-0x19-0

Living
19-0x15-4

Kit
12-6x15-4

Br 2/Study
13-9x12-4

Up

Foyer

Dining
11-8x12-8

Garage
20-0x34-0

© Copyright by designer/architect

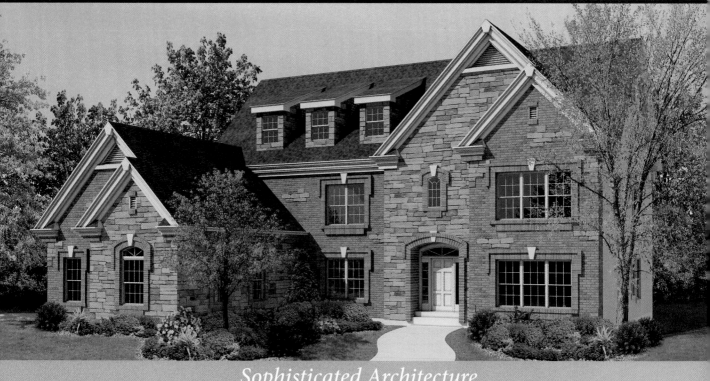

Sophisticated Architecture

- 3,974 total square feet of living area
- The exterior offers a look of distinction from the use of fancy brickwork to the old-world stone
- A fireplace and wood beam ceiling adorn the large great room
- The huge master bedroom features a vaulted ceiling, fireplace, two walk-in closets and a lavish bath
- 4 bedrooms, 3 1/2 baths, 3-car side entry garage
- Basement foundation

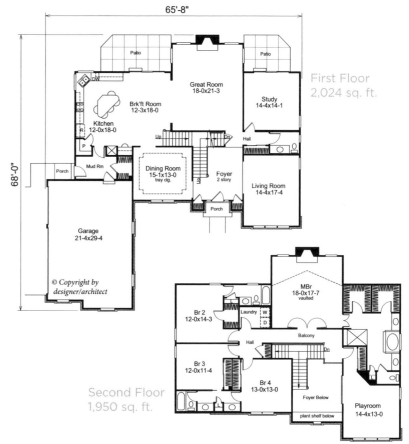

First Floor
2,024 sq. ft.

Second Floor
1,950 sq. ft.

Distinctive Home With Wrap-Around Porch And Deck

- 2,400 total square feet of living area
- Airy, spacious, highly-functional design for carefree living
- Master bedroom suite is located on the first floor for added privacy
- Extensive porch and deck combination for outdoor entertaining
- 3 bedrooms, 2 1/2 baths, 2-car garage
- Crawl space foundation

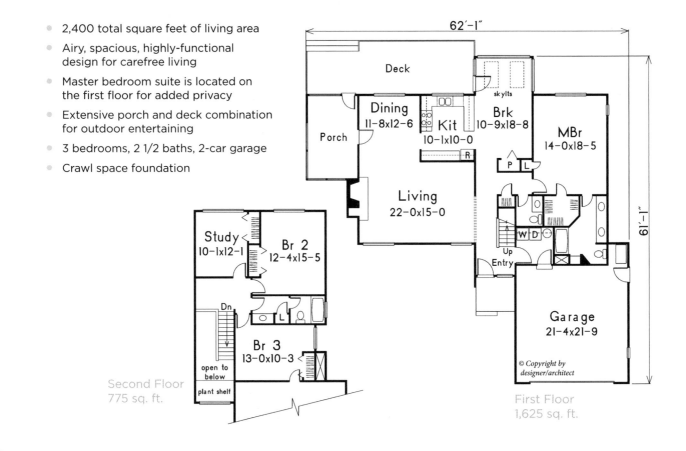

Second Floor
775 sq. ft.

First Floor
1,625 sq. ft.

LOWE'S LEGACY SERIES

Side Entry Garage Creates Expansive Exterior

- 2,610 total square feet of living space
- A 10' cabinet peninsula divides the large dining area from a functional kitchen featuring an abundance of storage and counterspace
- Bookshelves flanking a masonry fireplace adorn the end of the spacious family room
- All second floor bedrooms have ample storage
- Master bedroom includes two closets and a full bath
- Optional studio above the garage has an additional 254 square feet of living area
- 4 bedrooms, 2 1/2 baths, 2-car side entry garage
- Basement foundation

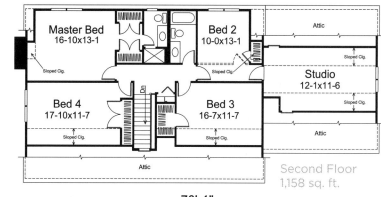

Master Bed 16-10x13-1
Bed 2 10-0x13-1
Attic
Sloped Clg.
Studio 12-1x11-6
Sloped Clg.
Bed 4 17-10x11-7
Bed 3 16-7x11-7
Sloped Clg.
Attic

Second Floor 1,158 sq. ft.

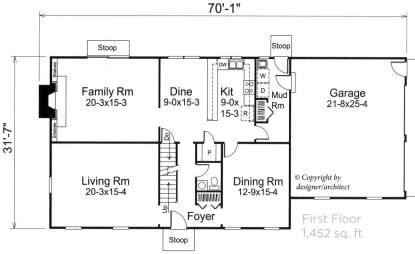

70'-1"

Stoop
Family Rm 20-3x15-3
Dine 9-0x15-3
Kit 9-0x 15-3
Mud Rm
Garage 21-8x25-4
Stoop
31'-7"
Living Rm 20-3x15-4
Dining Rm 12-9x15-4
Foyer
Stoop

© Copyright by designer/architect

First Floor 1,452 sq. ft.

Sun-Drenched Foyer Has Balcony Overlook

- 3,073 total square feet of living area
- Living room includes a bay window and opens to the dining room featuring a box-bay window seat
- Convenient kitchen overlooks breakfast nook that leads into the large family room with fireplace and sliding doors to the rear yard
- Huge master bedroom has a vaulted ceiling, large sitting area and a lavish bath
- All bedrooms have large closets and share a hall bath
- 4 bedrooms, 2 1/2 baths, 2-car side entry garage
- Basement foundation

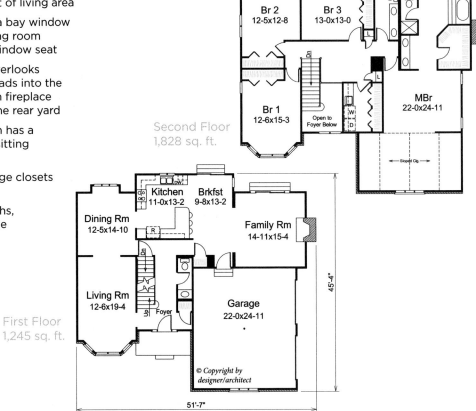

Second Floor
1,828 sq. ft.

First Floor
1,245 sq. ft.

Contemporary Style Home

- 2,005 total square feet of living area

- Enchanting covered courtyard entry is well lit with skylights

- The deck is accessible from the living room and master bedroom for easy outdoor living

- Formal dining room has a soffit ceiling with exquisite columns

- 3 bedrooms, 2 1/2 baths, 2-car garage

- Partial basement/crawl space foundation

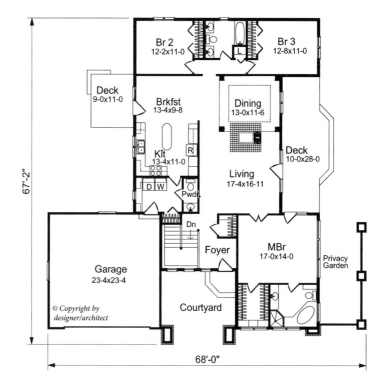

Balcony Enjoys Spectacular Views In Atrium Home

- 2,963 total square feet of living area
- Harmonious charm throughout
- A sweeping balcony and vaulted ceiling soar above the spacious great room and walk-in wet bar
- Atrium with lower level family room is a unique touch, creating an open and airy feeling
- 4 bedrooms, 2 1/2 baths, 2-car garage
- Walk-out basement foundation

First Floor
1,650 sq. ft.

Second Floor
1,053 sq. ft.

Lower Level
260 sq. ft.

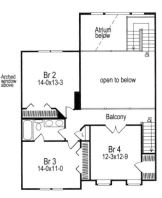

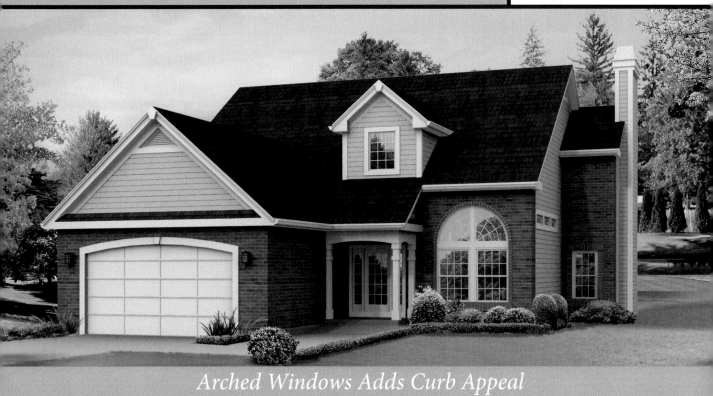

Arched Windows Adds Curb Appeal

- 2,360 total square feet of living area

- The U-shaped kitchen enjoys the convenience of a large walk-in pantry, desk area and extended counterspace with enough casual dining space for three people

- An enormous hearth room extends off the bayed breakfast area and features a cozy fireplace on one wall and an oversized bay window on another

- Terrific luxury can be found in the second floor master bedroom including his and her walk-in closets and a private bath with a corner spa style tub

- Balcony overlooks the spacious living room with large arched window and has views out the active dormer

- 3 bedrooms, 2 1/2 baths, 2-car garage

- Basement foundation

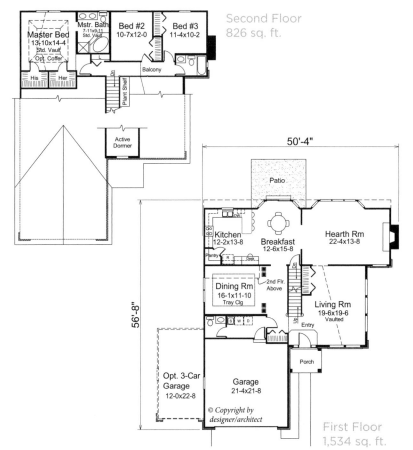

Charming Design Features Home Office

- 2,452 total square feet of living area

- Cheery and spacious home office room with private entrance and bath, two closets, vaulted ceiling and transomed window is perfect shown as a home office or a fourth bedroom

- Delightful great room features a vaulted ceiling, fireplace, extra storage closets and patio doors to the deck

- Extra-large kitchen features a walk-in pantry, cooktop island and bay window

- Vaulted master bedroom includes transomed windows, walk-in closet and luxurious bath

- 3 bedrooms, 2 1/2 baths, 3-car garage

- Basement foundation

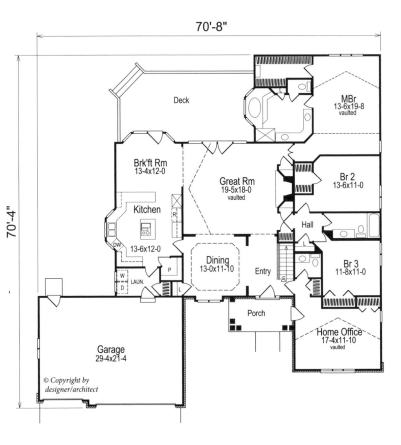

70'-8"

70'-4"

Deck

MBr
13-6x19-8
vaulted

Brk'ft Rm
13-4x12-0

Great Rm
19-5x18-0
vaulted

Br 2
13-6x11-0

Kitchen

13-6x12-0

Hall

Dining
13-0x11-10

Br 3
11-8x11-0

Entry

P

W
D LAUN.

L

Porch

Garage
29-4x21-4

Home Office
17-4x11-10
vaulted

© Copyright by
designer/architect

Decorative Roof Lines Add Character

- 2,343 total square feet of living area
- Energy efficient home with 2″ x 6″ exterior walls
- The spacious kitchen offers an abundance of counterspace including an extra-large center island
- A butler's pantry is located outside the formal dining room to assist with entertaining
- The airy living room features a cathedral ceiling and grand fireplace
- All bedrooms are located on the second floor for privacy
- 4 bedrooms, 2 1/2 baths, 3-car garage
- Basement foundation

Second Floor
1,166 sq. ft.

First Floor
1,177 sq. ft.

A Master Bedroom Second To None

- 4,465 total square feet of living area

- Arched double-entry 8' doors of this prestigious home lead you into a grand foyer with stately staircase and two overlooking second floor balconies

- The kitchen/breakfast area features a large center island, snack bar, menu desk, and cabinet pantries

- The master bedroom has a coffered ceiling, double-entry doors, huge walk-in closets and a lavish bath with whirlpool tub that overlooks the two-story atrium/exercise room

- A playroom and three generously-sized bedrooms comprise the second floor, each with a walk-in closet and access to an oversized bath

- 4 bedrooms, 3 1/2 baths, 3-car side entry garage

- Walk-out basement foundation

Second Floor
1,415 sq. ft.

First Floor
2,850 sq. ft.

Lower Level
200 sq. ft.

Luxurious Master Bedroom

- 2,805 total square feet of living area
- Wrap-around counter in the kitchen opens to a bayed breakfast area
- Great room features a grand fireplace flanked by doors that access the rear covered porch
- Secondary bedrooms enjoy walk-in closets
- The extra-large utility room offers an abundance of workspace
- 4 bedrooms, 3 baths, 2-car side entry garage
- Basement foundation, drawings also include crawl space and slab foundations

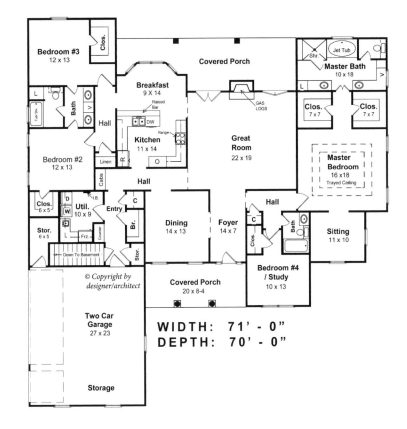

WIDTH: 71' - 0"
DEPTH: 70' - 0"

Ultimate Atrium For A Sloping Lot

- 3,810 total square feet of living area

- Massive sunken great room with vaulted ceiling includes exciting balcony overlook of towering atrium window wall

- Breakfast bar adjoins open "California" kitchen

- Seven vaulted rooms for drama and four fireplaces for warmth

- Master bath is complemented by the colonnade and fireplace surrounding the sunken tub and deck

- 3 bedrooms, 2 1/2 baths, 3-car side entry garage

- Walk-out basement foundation

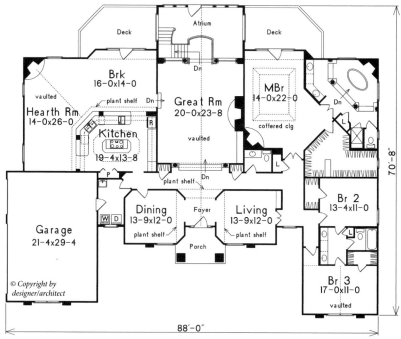

LOWE'S
LEGACY
SERIES

Charming House, Spacious And Functional

- 2,505 total square feet of living area
- The garage features an extra storage area and ample workspace
- Laundry room is accessible from the garage and the outdoors
- Deluxe raised tub and an immense walk-in closet grace the master bath
- 3 bedrooms, 2 1/2 baths, 2-car side entry garage
- Basement foundation, drawings also include crawl space foundation

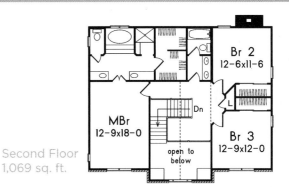

Second Floor
1,069 sq. ft.

Br 2
12-6x11-6

MBr
12-9x18-0

Dn

L

Br 3
12-9x12-0

open to
below

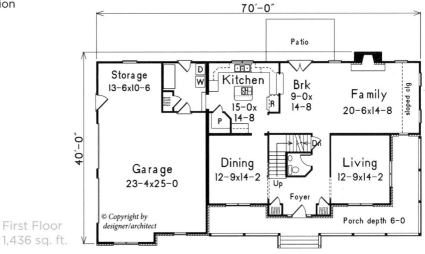

70'-0"

Patio

Storage
13-6x10-6

D
W

Kitchen
15-0x
14-8

Brk
9-0x
14-8

Family
20-6x14-8

sloped clg

P

R

40'-0"

Garage
23-4x25-0

Dining
12-9x14-2

Dn

Living
12-9x14-2

Up

Foyer

Porch depth 6-0

© Copyright by
designer/architect

First Floor
1,436 sq. ft.

Prestige Abounds In A Classic Ranch

- 2,723 total square feet of living area

- A large porch invites you into an elegant foyer which accesses a vaulted study with private hall and coat closet

- Great room is second to none, comprised of a fireplace, built-in shelves, vaulted ceiling and a 1 1/2 story window wall

- A spectacular hearth room with vaulted ceiling and masonry fireplace opens to an elaborate kitchen featuring two snack bars, a cooking island and walk-in pantry

- 3 bedrooms, 2 1/2 baths, 3-car side entry garage

- Basement foundation

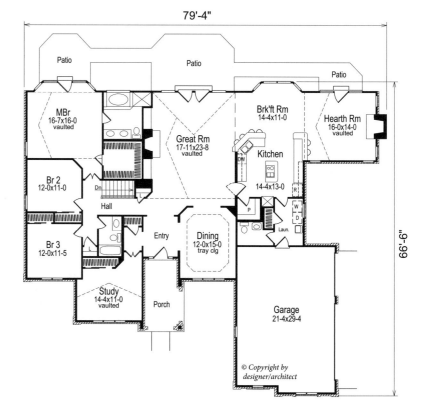

Large Patio And Pool For Entertaining

- 3,290 total square feet of living area

- Energy efficient home with 2″ x 6″ exterior walls

- Patio area surrounds the pool with a swim-up bar; both the pool and spa are great options with this plan

- Formal dining room features a dramatic drop down ceiling and easy access to the kitchen

- Fireplace provides a focal point in the master bedroom that includes a sitting room and elegant master bath

- An observation room and two bedrooms with adjoining bath are located on the second floor

- Varied ceiling heights throughout

- 4 bedrooms, 3 1/2 baths, 2-car side entry garage

- Slab foundation

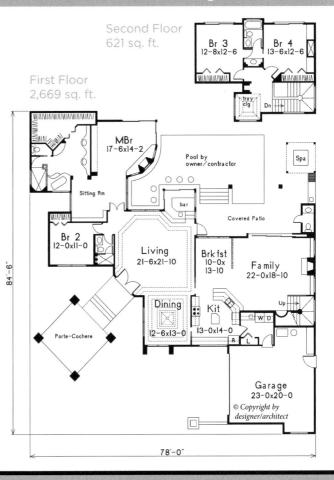

Second Floor
621 sq. ft.

First Floor
2,669 sq. ft.

Atrium Ranch With Sunroom

- 2,560 total square feet of living area

- A large front porch and entry leads to a vaulted great room featuring an atrium, fireplace and a massive two-story window wall

- The kitchen offers a snack bar peninsula, island counter and walk-in pantry

- Both covered and uncovered decks plus a sunroom are restful areas one may enjoy adjacent to the bayed breakfast room

- The master bedroom enjoys a coffered ceiling, bay window, plush bath and huge walk-in closet

- 3 bedrooms, 2 1/2 baths, 3-car side entry garage

- Walk-out basement foundation

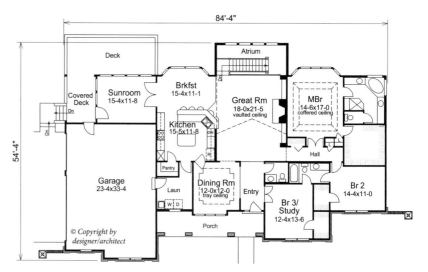

84'-4"

54'-4"

Deck

Covered Deck

Sunroom
15-4x11-8

Brkfst
15-4x11-1

Atrium

Great Rm
18-0x21-5
vaulted ceiling

MBr
14-6x17-0
coffered ceiling

Kitchen
15-5x11-8

Pantry

Garage
23-4x33-4

Laun
W D

Dining Rm
12-0x12-0
tray ceiling

Entry

Hall

Br 3/
Study
12-4x13-6

Br 2
14-4x11-0

Porch

© Copyright by designer/architect

LOWE'S
LEGACY
SERIES

Striking Balcony Overlooks Great Room And Kitchen

- 2,501 total square feet of living area

- Oversized kitchen/breakfast area has a work island, vaulted ceiling and plant shelves

- An open staircase overlooks the kitchen/breakfast area

- Secluded second floor guest bedroom features private half bath

- Covered deck is accessible from the dining room and kitchen

- 4 bedrooms, 2 1/2 baths, 2-car side entry garage

- Basement foundation, drawings also include crawl space and slab foundations

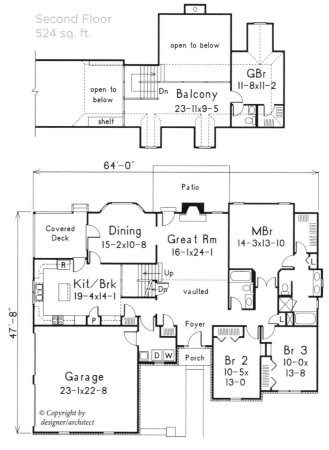

Second Floor
524 sq. ft.

open to below

open to below

GBr
11-8x11-2

Balcony
23-11x9-5

Dn

shelf

64'-0"

Patio

Covered Deck

Dining
15-2x10-8

Great Rm
16-1x24-1

MBr
14-3x13-10

Kit/Brk
19-4x14-1

Up
Dn

vaulted

47'-8"

R

P

Foyer

Garage
23-1x22-8

D W

Porch

Br 2
10-5x13-0

Br 3
10-0x13-8

© Copyright by designer/architect

First Floor
1,977 sq. ft.

Arch Windows Grace Magnificent Facade

- 2,993 total square feet of living area

- 10' ceilings on the first floor,
  9' ceilings on the second floor

- Second floor bedrooms
  include private dressing areas,
  walk-in closets and share a bath

- Generous family room and kitchen
  combine for a central activity area

- 4 bedrooms, 3 baths, 2-car
  side entry detached garage

- Slab foundation, drawings also
  include crawl space foundation

Second Floor
624 sq. ft.

First Floor
2,369 sq. ft.

Garage
20-4x21-6

© Copyright by
designer/architect

Country Ranch Enjoys Large Great Room

- 1,944 total square feet of living area

- Spacious surrounding porch, covered patio and stone fireplace create an expansive ponderosa appearance

- The large entry leads to a grand-sized great room featuring a vaulted ceiling, fireplace, wet bar and access to the porch through three patio doors

- The U-shaped kitchen is open to the hearth room and enjoys a snack bar, fireplace and patio access

- A luxury bath, walk-in closet and doors to the porch are a few of the amenities of the master bedroom

- 3 bedrooms, 2 baths, 3-car detached garage

- Basement foundation

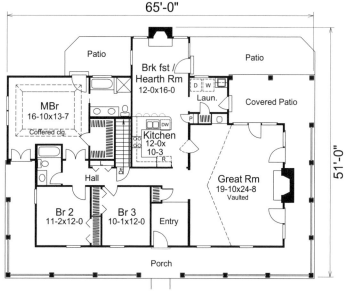

Cozy Breakfast Bay With Full Outside View

- 2,397 total square feet of living area
- Varied ceiling heights throughout home
- All bedrooms boast walk-in closets
- Garage includes convenient storage area
- Angled kitchen counter overlooks the spacious living room with fireplace
- Master bedroom has a coffered ceiling and luxurious bath
- 4 bedrooms, 3 baths, 2-car side entry garage
- Slab foundation

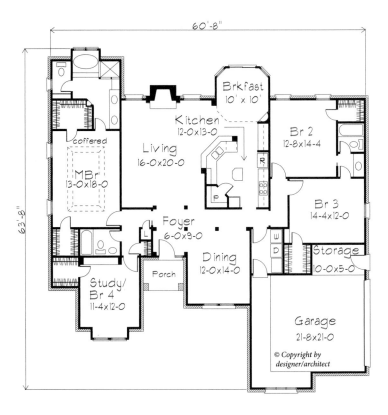

© Copyright by designer/architect

Enchanting Courtyard Brings the Outdoors In

- 2,254 total square feet of living area

- The expansive front porch has a large planter box and protection from the elements

- A spacious entry with guest closet welcomes you into a huge vaulted great room with fireplace and two 9' sliding glass doors that view the center courtyard

- A 10' high coffered ceiling, sliding doors to the courtyard, two walk-in closets, luxury bath with separate shower and a sumptuous spa area with several windows viewing the courtyard are the many exciting features of the master bedroom

- 3 bedrooms, 2 1/2 baths, 2-car rear entry garage

- Slab foundation

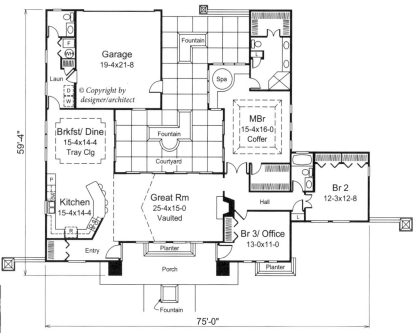

Centrally Located Great Room

- 2,024 total square feet of living area
- Covered porches offer a relaxing atmosphere
- Bedrooms are separated for privacy
- The formal dining room provides an elegant space for entertaining
- The second floor living area and optional bath are ideal for a guest suite
- 3 bedrooms, 2 baths, 2-car side entry garage
- Basement foundation, drawings also include slab and crawl space foundations

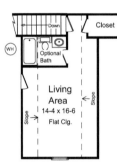

Second Floor
386 sq. ft.

First Floor
1,638 sq. ft.

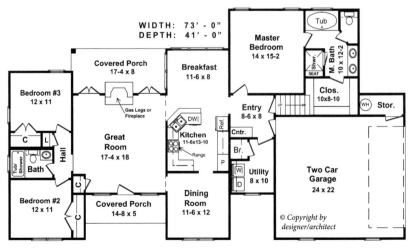

Bay Creates Bright Sunroom

- 2,148 total square feet of living area
- Cheerful bayed sunroom has an attached porch and overlooks the kitchen and breakfast area
- Varied ceiling heights throughout the entire plan
- All bedrooms have walk-in closets
- Laundry area includes handy sink
- Optional bonus room on the second floor has an additional 336 square feet of living area
- 3 bedrooms, 2 1/2 baths, 2-car side entry garage
- Basement foundation

Width: 54'-7"
Depth: 62'-8"

First Floor
1,626 sq. ft.

Second Floor
522 sq. ft.

Classic Elegance

- 2,483 total square feet of living area

- A large entry porch with open brick arches and palladian door welcomes guests

- The vaulted great room features an entertainment center alcove and the ideal layout for furniture placement

- The dining room is extra large with a stylish tray ceiling

- A convenient kitchen with wrap-around counter, menu desk and pantry opens to the cozy breakfast area

- 2″ x 6″ exterior walls available, please order plan #542-007E-0062

- Plan also available with energy efficient R-Control® SIPs (Structural Insulated Panels), please call 1-877-379-3420 for more information

- 3 bedrooms, 2 baths, 2-car side entry garage

- Basement foundation

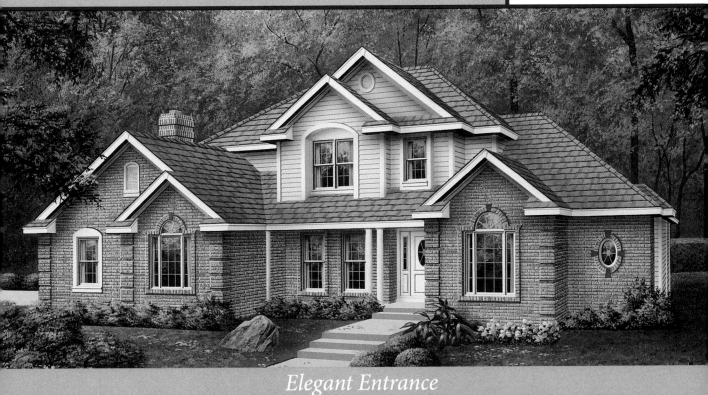

Elegant Entrance

- 3,357 total square feet of living area
- Attractive balcony overlooks entry foyer and living area
- Balcony area could easily convert to a fifth bedroom
- Spacious kitchen also opens into a sunken family room with a fireplace
- First floor master bedroom boasts a large walk-in closet and dressing area
- Central laundry room has a laundry chute from the second floor
- 4 bedrooms, 2 full baths, 2 half baths, 2-car side entry garage
- Basement foundation, drawings also include crawl space and slab foundations

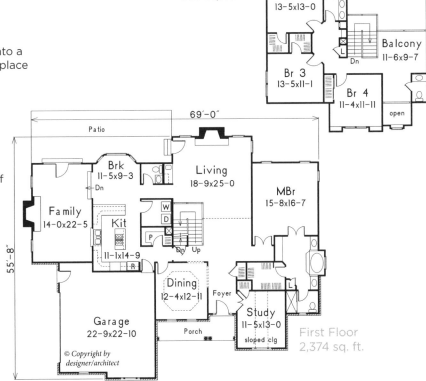

Second Floor
983 sq. ft.

Br 2
13-5x13-0

sloped clg

open to below

Balcony
11-6x9-7

Dn

Br 3
13-5x11-1

Br 4
11-4x11-11

open

69'-0"

Patio

Brk
11-5x9-3

Living
18-9x25-0

Dn

MBr
15-8x16-7

Family
14-0x22-5

W
D

Kit
11-1x14-9

P

Dn Up

55'-8"

R

Dining
12-4x12-11

Foyer

Garage
22-9x22-10

Porch

Study
11-5x13-0
sloped clg

First Floor
2,374 sq. ft.

© Copyright by
designer/architect

Grand Arched Entry

- 2,564 total square feet of living area

- Hearth room is surrounded by the kitchen, dining and breakfast rooms making it the focal point of these living areas

- Escape to the master bedroom featuring a luxurious private bath and a sitting area leading to the deck outdoors

- The secondary bedrooms share a Jack and Jill bath and both have a walk-in closet

- 3 bedrooms, 2 1/2 baths, 2-car side entry garage

- Basement foundation, drawings also include slab and crawl space foundations

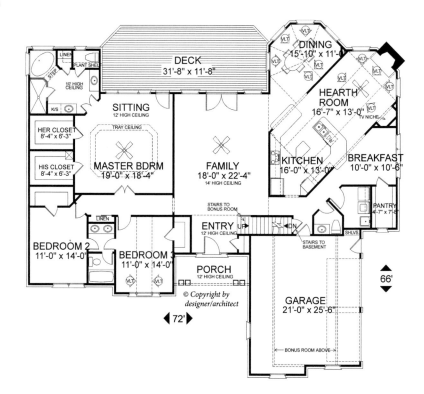

© Copyright by designer/architect

Atrium Ranch With True Pizzazz

- 2,398 total square feet of living area

- A grand entry porch leads to a dramatic vaulted entry foyer with a plant shelf open to the great room

- The great room enjoys a 12' vaulted ceiling, atrium featuring 2 1/2 story windows and fireplace with flanking bookshelves

- A conveniently located sunroom and side porch adjoin the breakfast room and garage

- 763 square feet of optional living area on the lower level with family room, bedroom #4 and bath

- 2" x 6" exterior walls available, please order plan #542-007E-0098

- Plan also available with energy efficient R-Control® SIPs (Structural Insulated Panels), please call 1-877-379-3420 for more information

- 3 bedrooms, 2 baths, 3-car side entry garage

- Walk-out basement foundation

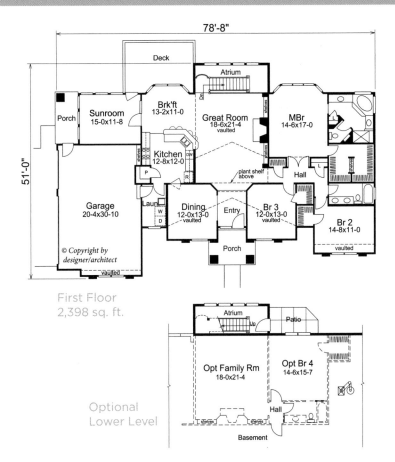

First Floor
2,398 sq. ft.

Optional
Lower Level

Terrific Master Bedroom Provides Escape

- 2,517 total square feet of living area

- Energy efficient home with 2" x 6" exterior walls

- Central living room with large windows and attractive transoms

- Varied ceiling heights throughout home

- Secluded master bedroom features double-door entry, luxurious bath with separate shower, step-up whirlpool tub, double vanities and walk-in closets

- Kitchen with walk-in pantry overlooks large family room with fireplace and unique octagon-shaped breakfast room

- 4 bedrooms, 2 1/2 baths, 2-car garage

- Slab foundation, drawings also include crawl space foundation

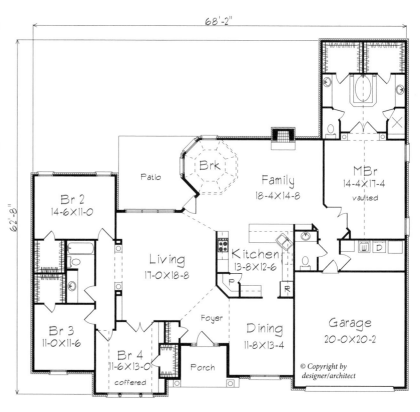

© Copyright by designer/architect

Wonderful Open Great Room

- 2,307 total square feet of living area
- The bayed breakfast area warms the home with natural light
- The spacious master bedroom boasts two walk-in closets, a private bath and a bonus area ideal for an office or nursery
- The vaulted great room includes a grand fireplace, built-in shelves and a double-door entry onto the covered porch
- 3 bedrooms, 2 1/2 baths, 2-car side entry garage
- Basement foundation, drawings also include crawl space and slab foundations

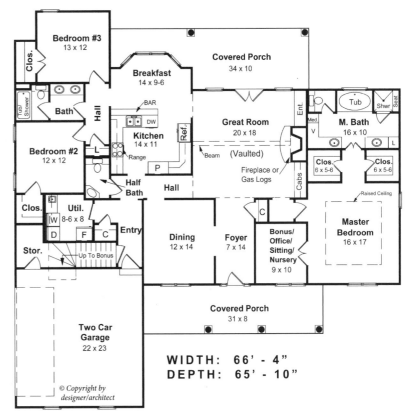

Bedroom #3
13 x 12

Breakfast
14 x 9-6

Covered Porch
34 x 10

Bath

Kitchen
14 x 11

Great Room
20 x 18

M. Bath
16 x 10

Bedroom #2
12 x 12

Half Bath

Hall

(Vaulted)

Fireplace or
Gas Logs

Clos.
6 x 5-6

Clos.
6 x 5-6

Raised Ceiling

Util.
8-6 x 8

Entry

Dining
12 x 14

Foyer
7 x 14

**Bonus/
Office/
Sitting/
Nursery**
9 x 10

**Master
Bedroom**
16 x 17

Stor.

Up To Bonus

Covered Porch
31 x 8

**Two Car
Garage**
22 x 23

© Copyright by
designer/architect

WIDTH: 66' - 4"
DEPTH: 65' - 10"

Vaulted Ceilings Enhance Spacious Home

- 2,073 total square feet of living area
- Family room provides an ideal gathering area with a fireplace, large windows and vaulted ceiling
- Private first floor master bedroom enjoys a vaulted ceiling and luxury bath
- Kitchen features an angled bar connecting it to the breakfast area
- 4 bedrooms, 2 1/2 baths, 2-car side entry garage
- Basement foundation

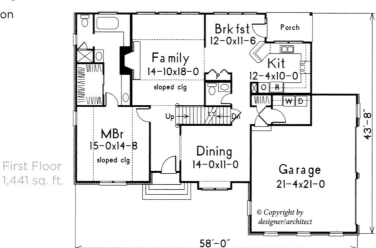

Second Floor
632 sq. ft.

First Floor
1,441 sq. ft.

Sunroom And Two Covered Porches

- 2,800 total square feet of living area

- Handsome exterior offers a large front porch ideal for relaxing

- The vaulted living and dining rooms feature a fireplace, bay window overlooking the rear porch and are open to a sensational kitchen with snack bar and center island

- The spacious master bedroom with coffered ceiling has both his and hers baths with walk-in closets

- A sunroom, perfect for informal gatherings, is adjacent to the rear covered porch and provides access to a mud room, stairs to the basement and the rear garage

- Also included is a layout for an optional basement apartment with 932 square feet of living area

- 3 bedrooms, 3 baths, 2-car side entry garage

- Walk-out basement foundation

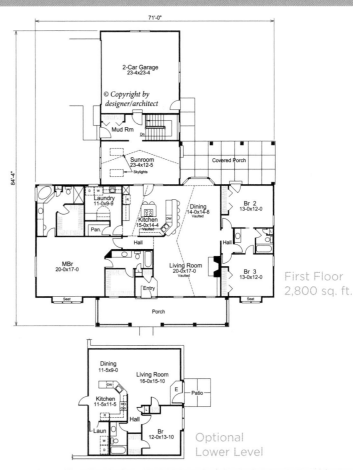

First Floor
2,800 sq. ft.

Optional
Lower Level

Large Open Deck

- 3,271 total square feet of living area
- The grand room features a handsome fireplace framed by French doors on both sides leading out to the deck
- The see-through fireplace gives the master bedroom a natural focal point
- The second floor balcony overlooks the grand room
- A bonus room/bedroom #5 above the garage allows for an additional 412 square feet of living area
- 4 bedrooms, 4 1/2 baths, 3-car side entry garage
- Walk-out basement foundation

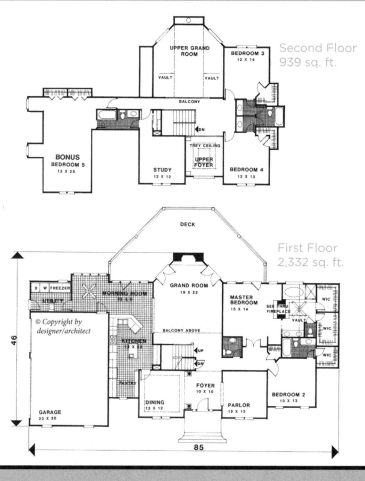

Second Floor
939 sq. ft.

First Floor
2,332 sq. ft.

Magnificent Manor Home

- 3,160 total square feet of living area
- Covered entry porch leads into a magnificent two-story foyer that accesses formal rooms on either side
- First floor master bedroom features two walk-in closets and a large master bath
- Kitchen is designed for efficiency and includes island cooktop and pass-through to the breakfast room
- 4 bedrooms, 3 1/2 baths, 3-car side entry garage
- Basement foundation

Second Floor
939 sq. ft.

Br 4
15-3x11-0

open to below

Br 3
11-8x11-7

Br 2
12-11x13-6

open to below

First Floor
2,221 sq. ft.

57'-0"

Deck

Brk
13-0x11-8

Bar

Family
18-0x25-3

MBr
17-0x13-11
coffered clg

Kitchen

R

12-6x16-4

W
D

P

Dining
11-7x15-7

Dn
Up

Living
14-0x15-4
vaulted

64'-4"

Garage
20-9x30-0

Porch

© Copyright by designer/architect

Organized Kitchen Is The Center Of Activity

- 1,882 total square feet of living area

- Handsome brick facade

- Spacious great room and dining area combination is brightened by unique corner windows and patio access

- Well-designed kitchen incorporates a breakfast bar peninsula, sweeping casement window above sink and a walk-in pantry island

- Master bedroom features a large walk-in closet and private bath with bay window

- Plan also available with energy efficient R-Control® SIPs (Structural Insulated Panels), please call 1-877-379-3420 for more information

- 4 bedrooms, 2 baths, 2-car side entry garage

- Basement foundation

LOWE'S
LEGACY
SERIES

Arched Elegance

- 3,222 total square feet of living area

- Two-story foyer features a central staircase and views to the second floor, dining and living rooms

- Built-in breakfast booth is surrounded by windows

- Gourmet kitchen includes a view to the great room

- Two-story great room features a large fireplace and arched openings to the second floor

- Elegant master bedroom has a separate reading room with bookshelves and fireplace

- 4 bedrooms, 3 1/2 baths, 2-car side entry garage

- Basement foundation, drawings also include crawl space and slab foundations

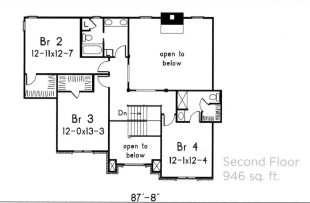

Second Floor
946 sq. ft.

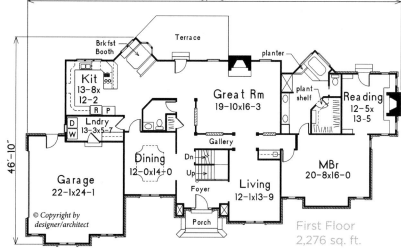

First Floor
2,276 sq. ft.

Rambling Home With Traditional Elegance

- 2,518 total square feet of living area
- Expansive kitchen is adjacent to the bayed breakfast room
- Sophisticated master bedroom is complemented by double closets and a luxury bath
- Family room enjoys rear views and a stately fireplace
- Side porch leads to the mud room with laundry, utility sink and coat closet
- 4 bedrooms, 2 1/2 baths, 2-car side entry garage
- Partial basement/crawl space foundation, drawings also include crawl space and slab foundations

First Floor
1,702 sq. ft.

Second Floor
816 sq. ft.

© Copyright by designer/architect

Great Covered Patio For Outdoor Living

- 2,487 total square feet of living area

- Beautiful vaulted master bedroom feaures a spacious bath and direct access to a private patio

- A see-through fireplace illuminates both the hearth/dining area and the breakfast room while acting as the main focal point in both spaces

- A trio of windows, 10' ceiling height and a corner fireplace create a pleasant atmosphere in the great room

- 3 bedrooms, 2 1/2 baths, 2-car garage

- Basement foundation

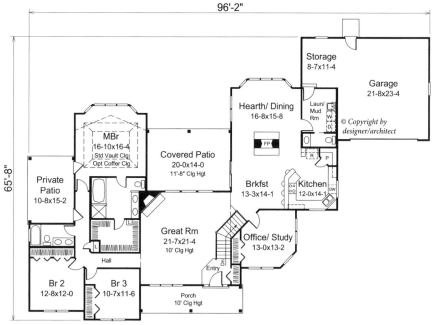

Stately Elegance

- 3,657 total square feet of living area

- Dramatic two-story entry has a stylish niche, a convenient powder room and French doors leading to the parlor

- State-of-the-art kitchen includes a large walk-in pantry, breakfast island, computer center and 40' vista through family room with walk-in wet bar

- Vaulted master bath features marble steps and Roman columns that lead to a majestic-sized whirlpool tub with a surrounding marble deck and grand-scale palladian window

- A Jack and Jill bath, hall bath, loft area and huge bedrooms comprise the second floor

- 4 bedrooms, 3 1/2 baths, 3-car side entry garage

- Basement foundation

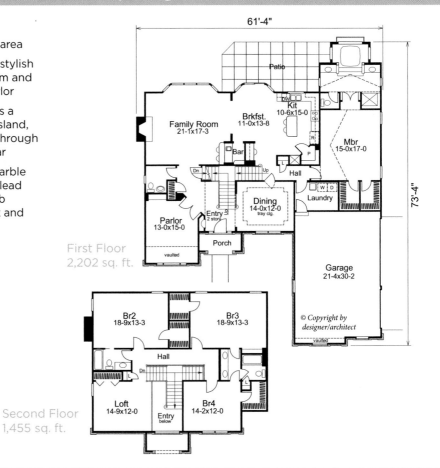

First Floor
2,202 sq. ft.

Second Floor
1,455 sq. ft.

LOWE'S
LEGACY
SERIES

Shingle Style Two-Story Southern Home

- 2,698 total square feet of living area

- A rear screened porch creates an outdoor extension off the family room

- The curved counter in the kitchen overlooks the breakfast and family rooms merging all the spaces together

- The second floor bedroom #4 or library has a window seat flanked by closet space making it ideal as a home office

- 5 bedrooms, 5 baths, 4-car side entry garage

- Basement foundation

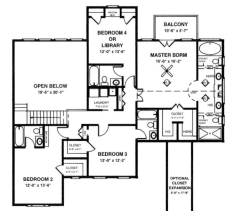

Second Floor
1,454 sq. ft.

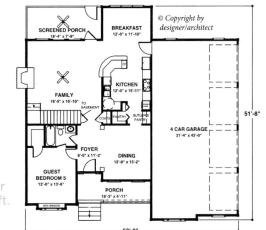

First Floor
1,244 sq. ft.

Designed For Family Living

- 2,224 total square feet of living area
- The covered porch welcomes all into this lovely two-story home
- A snack bar island and walk-in pantry add efficiency to the open kitchen
- The second floor master bedroom enjoys a luxurious bath with twin vanities, a whirlpool tub and massive walk-in closet
- 3 bedrooms, 2 1/2 baths, 2-car garage
- Basement foundation

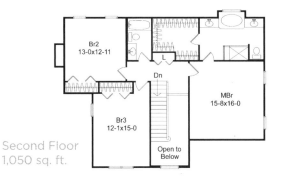

Second Floor
1,050 sq. ft.

Br2
13-0x12-11

Br3
12-1x15-0

Dn

L

Open to Below

MBr
15-8x16-0

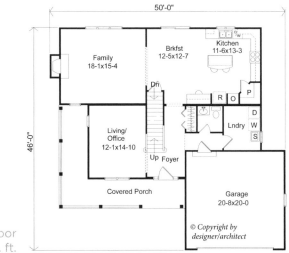

First Floor
1,174 sq. ft.

50'-0"

46'-0"

Family
18-1x15-4

Brkfst
12-5x12-7

Kitchen
11-6x13-3

Living/Office
12-1x14-10

Lndry

R O P

D W S

Dn

Up Foyer

Covered Porch

Garage
20-8x20-0

© Copyright by designer/architect

LEGACY SERIES

Lower Level Is Great For Entertaining

- 3,411 total square feet of living area
- Foyer opens to a large study with raised ceiling
- Master bedroom features an octagon-shaped raised ceiling and private bath with double vanities and corner whirlpool tub
- Expansive windows and a two-way fireplace enhance the great room
- 3 bedrooms, 3 baths, 3-car garage
- Basement foundation

First Floor
2,182 sq. ft.

Lower Level
1,229 sq. ft.

Spectacular Five Bedroom Home

- 2,801 total square feet of living area
- 9' ceilings on the first floor
- Full view dining bay with elegant circle-top windows
- Wrap-around porches provide outdoor exposure in all directions
- Secluded master bedroom with double vanities and walk-in closets
- Convenient second floor game room
- 5 bedrooms, 3 baths, 2-car side entry garage
- Slab foundation

45'-6"

78'-3"

Garage
23-4x23-4

© Copyright by designer/architect

Covered Porch

Living
18-0x17-3

MBr
17-0x16-0

Brk
10-0x10-0

Kit
10-8x12-0

Br 2
13-0x10-6

Dining
10-8x13-4

Porch Depth 4-0

Up

D W P R

First Floor
1,651 sq. ft.

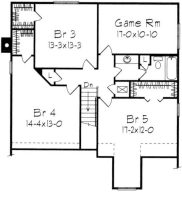

Second Floor
1,150 sq. ft.

Br 3
13-3x13-3

Game Rm
17-0x10-10

Br 4
14-4x13-0

Dn

Br 5
17-2x12-0

• To Order See Page 288 or Call Toll-Free 1-877-379-3420

Grand-Sized Living

- 3,366 total square feet of living area
- Wonderful covered patio is located off the secluded study and breakfast area
- Separate dining area for entertaining
- Spacious master bedroom has an enormous private bath with walk-in closet
- 4 bedrooms, 3 1/2 baths, 2-car side entry garage
- Crawl space foundation, drawings also include slab foundation

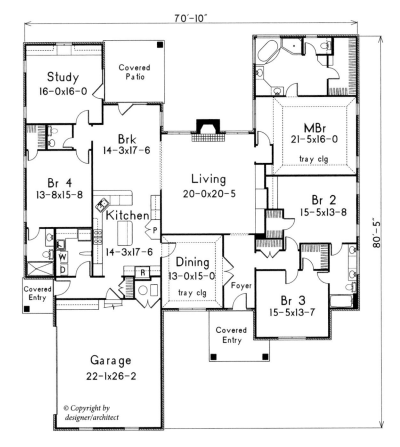

High Style With Central Kitchen

- 3,003 total square feet of living area

- Energy efficient home with 2" x 6" exterior walls

- Vaulted master bedroom features a large walk-in closet, spa tub, separate shower room and access to the rear patio

- Covered entrance opens into the foyer with a large greeting area

- Formal living room has a 12' ceiling and 36" walls on two sides

- Island kitchen features a large pantry and nook

- Cozy fireplace accents the vaulted family room that opens onto a covered deck

- Utility room with generous space is adjacent to a half bath

- 3 bedrooms, 2 1/2 baths, 3-car garage

- Crawl space foundation

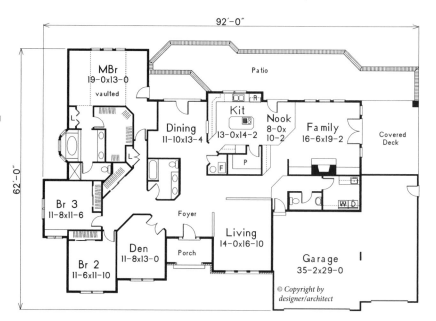

Two-Story Solarium Welcomes The Sun

- 3,850 total square feet of living area
- Entry, with balcony above, leads into a splendid great room with sunken solarium
- Kitchen layout boasts a half-circle bar and cooktop island with banquet-sized dining nearby
- Solarium features U-shaped staircase with balcony and an arched window
- Master bedroom includes a luxurious bath and large study with bay window
- 5 bedrooms, 3 1/2 baths, 3-car garage
- Basement foundation

Second Floor
1,544 sq. ft.

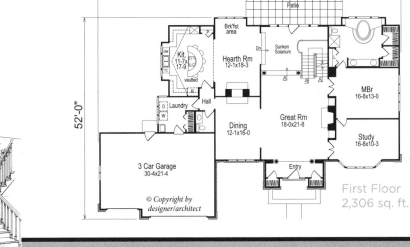

First Floor
2,306 sq. ft.

Timeless Appeal, This Home Has Luxurious Comforts

- 5,321 total square feet of living area
- The combination of stone, brick, multiple gables and roof dormers creates an exciting and sophisticated structure
- A two-story entry foyer and wide, finely crafted staircase with niche is inviting and elegant
- The kitchen includes a bayed breakfast room, hearth room with fireplace and is convenient to a large dining room with butler's pantry
- The master bedroom with sitting room and sumptuous bath is unsurpassed in luxury
- 4 bedrooms, 5 1/2 baths, 3-car rear entry garage
- Basement foundation

Second Floor
1,784 sq. ft.

Br 2
15-1x12-0

Br 3
16-1x13-1

Family Room
21-1x20-9

Bar

Corridor

Laundry

Sitting

Seat

Br 4
14-4x13-0

Entry
Below

Balcony

First Floor
3,537 sq. ft.

Patio

Patio

Hearth Rm
15-4x15-3

Seat

Brk fst
15-5x11-4

Pantry

Great Room
21-5x20-7

Kitchen
15-9x15-4

MBr
15-0x18-0
coffered clg.

Garage
33-4x21-4

© Copyright by designer/architect

Laundry/
Mud Room

Hall

Dining
14-0x17-0
tray clg.

Entry
15-1x13-0

Hall

Sitting
9-8x12-4

Exercise Rm
13-4x14-3

Butler's
Pantry

Porch

Living Rm
12-4x16-0

Storage

109'-0"

65'-8"

Charming Breakfast Area

- 2,207 total square feet of living area
- The spacious great room boasts a 12' ceiling and corner fireplace
- The kitchen connects to the breakfast area and great room with an eating bar
- Extra storage is located in the garage
- 4 bedrooms, 2 1/2 baths, 2-car side entry garage
- Basement foundation, drawings also include crawl space and slab foundations

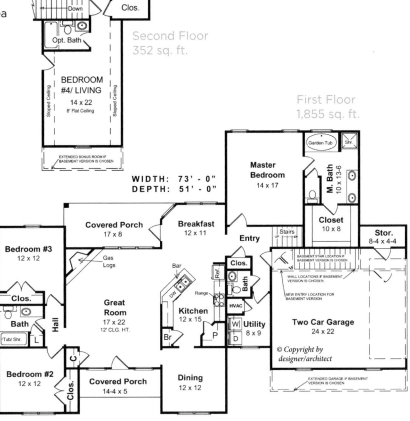

Second Floor 352 sq. ft.

Down | Clos.

Opt. Bath

BEDROOM #4/ LIVING
14 x 22
8' Flat Ceiling
Sloped Ceiling

EXTENDED BONUS ROOM IF BASEMENT VERSION IS CHOSEN

First Floor 1,855 sq. ft.

WIDTH: 73' - 0"
DEPTH: 51' - 0"

Master Bedroom 14 x 17

Garden Tub | Shr
M. Bath 10 x 13-6

Closet 10 x 8

Stor. 8-4 x 4-4

Covered Porch 17 x 8

Breakfast 12 x 11

Entry

Stairs
UP

BASEMENT STAIR LOCATION IF BASEMENT VERSION IS CHOSEN

Bedroom #3 12 x 12

Gas Logs

Bar

Ref.

Clos.

Bath

WALL LOCATIONS IF BASEMENT VERSION IS CHOSEN.

NEW ENTRY LOCATION FOR BASEMENT VERSION

Clos.

Bath

Tub/ Shr.

Hall

Great Room 17 x 22 12' CLG. HT.

DW
Range

Kitchen 12 x 15

HVAC

Utility 8 x 9
W
D

Two Car Garage 24 x 22

© Copyright by designer/architect

Br

P

Bedroom #2 12 x 12

Clos.
C

Covered Porch 14-4 x 5

Dining 12 x 12

EXTENDED GARAGE IF BASEMENT VERSION IS CHOSEN

Ideal Home For Lake Retreat

- 1,763 total square feet of living area

- Prairie style exterior with an elegant sophistication

- The entry foyer with glass double doors and a 10' volume ceiling has a convenient guest closet

- A corner fireplace and 9' glass sliding doors to the rear patio make the huge great room very inviting

- The L-shaped kitchen has cabinets galore and features a snack bar, menu desk, cabinet pantry and adjacent breakfast room, laundry room and half bath

- Double-entry doors, a luxury bath, large walk-in closet and glass door to a second private patio are a few of the amenities of the master bedroom

- 3 bedrooms, 2 1/2 baths, 2-car side garage

- Slab foundation, drawings also include basement and crawl space foundations

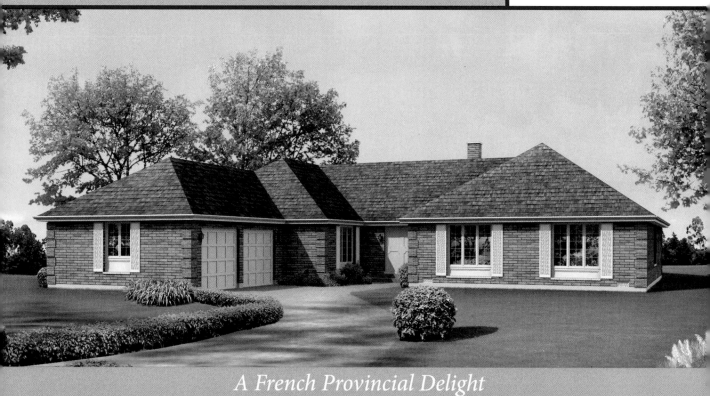

A French Provincial Delight

- 3,108 total square feet of living area
- Cheery living room glows with wide bow window
- Unusually large dining room features a coffered ceiling
- Located near the kitchen is the spacious mud room with laundry facilities, full bath, coat closets, storage pantry and stairs to the basement
- Master bedroom features a coffered ceiling and bath with skylight
- 4 bedrooms, 3 baths, 2-car side entry garage
- Partial basement/crawl space foundation, drawings also include crawl space foundation

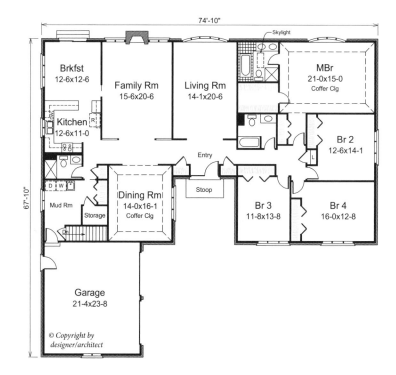

Peaceful Screened Porch For Relaxing

- 2,253 total square feet of living area
- Two bedrooms on the second floor share a bath
- Two walk-in closets, a private bath and a sitting area leading to an outdoor deck are all amenities of the master suite
- Bonus room on the second floor has an additional 247 square feet of living area
- 4 bedrooms, 3 baths, 2-car side entry garage
- Walk-out basement foundation, drawings also include slab and crawl space foundations

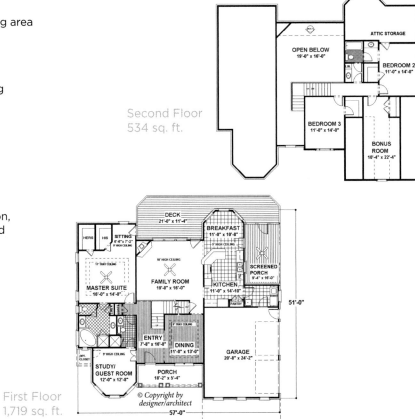

Second Floor
534 sq. ft.

First Floor
1,719 sq. ft.

© Copyright by designer/architect

Impressive Ranch Features Attractive Courtyard

- 2,851 total square feet of living area

- Foyer with double-door entrance leads to a unique sunken living room with patio view

- Multi-purpose room is perfect for a home office, hobby room or fifth bedroom

- Master bedroom boasts abundant closet space and access to the patio

- Family room has access to the kitchen and features a fireplace flanked by windows

- 4 bedrooms, 3 baths, 2-car garage

- Basement foundation, drawings also include crawl space and slab foundations

78'-10"

63'-5"

Family Rm
15-4x17-8

Patio

MBr
13-1x17-11

Multi-Purpose
Rm
11-8x11-9

Brkfst
6-3x8-9

Kitchen
12-8x16-5

Living Rm
17-1x15-4

Br 3
12-0x12-0

Shelves

Garage
21-4x21-8

Dining Rm
12-8x12-7

Foyer

Br 4/
Study
11-10x10-2

Br 2
15-9x12-0

© Copyright by
designer/architect

Courtyard

A Substantial Home With Luxurious Touches

- 2,820 total square feet of living area
- Convenient wet bar is located between the kitchen and the breakfast/family room
- Breakfast/kitchen and large family room flow together for informal entertaining
- Luxurious master bedroom suite enjoys a fireplace and generous closet
- Oversized foyer leads to private living and dining rooms
- 4 bedrooms, 2 1/2 baths, 2-car garage
- Basement foundation, drawings also include slab and crawl space foundations

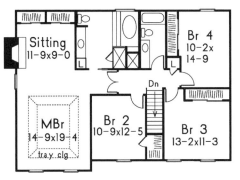

Second Floor
1,312 sq. ft.

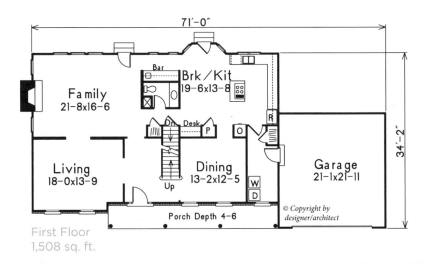

First Floor
1,508 sq. ft.

Terrific Custom-Style Victorian Makes Impression

- 2,560 total square feet of living area
- Numerous bay windows create a design unlike any other
- Enormous master bedroom has a private bath with step-up tub-in-a-bay
- Second floor laundry room is located near all the bedrooms
- Cheerful breakfast area extends onto the covered private porch
- 4 bedrooms, 2 1/2 baths, 2-car garage
- Basement foundation

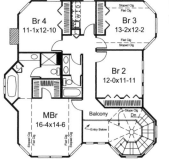

Second Floor
1,215 sq. ft.

Br 4
11-1x12-10

Br 3
13-2x12-2

Br 2
12-0x11-11

MBr
16-4x14-6

Balcony

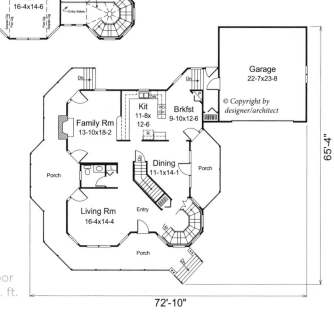

Garage
22-7x23-8

© Copyright by
designer/architect

Kit
11-8x
12-6

Brkfst
9-10x12-6

Family Rm
13-10x18-2

Dining
11-1x14-1

Porch

Porch

Living Rm
16-4x14-4

Entry

Porch

65'-4"

First Floor
1,345 sq. ft.

72'-10"

Interesting Roof Lines And Appealing Use Of Brick

- 2,520 total square feet of living area
- Open hearth fireplace warms the family and breakfast rooms
- Master bedroom features a private bath with deluxe tub, double-bowl vanity and large walk-in closet
- Vaulted living and dining rooms flank the foyer
- Corner sink in kitchen overlooks the family and breakfast rooms
- 4 bedrooms, 2 1/2 baths, 2-car side entry garage
- Basement foundation, drawings also include crawl space and slab foundations

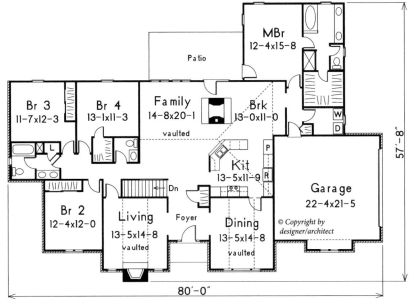

Beautiful Brick And Stone

- 2,953 total square feet of living area

- Craftsman details warm the entry with stone accents and a covered porch

- The open floor plan features both a family room and hearth room that leads to a screen porch

- A hidden room, cleverly concealed behind cabinet doors is located off the breakfast room providing space for a safe room, storage of valuables or security

- 4 bedrooms, 4 baths, 3-car side entry garage

- Basement foundation

Second Floor
1,367 sq. ft.

First Floor
1,586 sq. ft.

Classic Elegance

- 3,670 total square feet of living area

- Multiple gables, detailed brickwork and front patio establish an impressive facade

- Two-story entry has a handcrafted staircase and leads to a fabulous great room with fireplace flanked by shelving

- The kitchen features a snack bar island, computer desk, breakfast room with bay window and a walk-in pantry

- An awesome bath with two huge walk-in closets accompanies the master bedroom suite

- The second floor is comprised of three bedrooms, each with their own bath and walk-in closets as well as an open playroom with balcony overlook

- 4 bedrooms, 4 1/2 baths, 3-car side entry garage

- Basement foundation

Plan #542-007D-0152 • Price Code F

Second Floor
1,347 sq. ft.

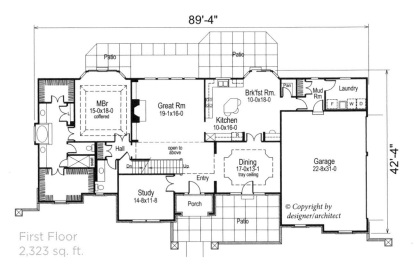

First Floor
2,323 sq. ft.

Masterfully Designed

- 4,465 total square feet of living area

- Brickwork and randomly placed stone, multiple gables, hip roofs, and board and batten shutters all contribute to this classic exterior

- The welcoming entry takes you into the great room with views of the rear deck, a dining room with tray ceiling and a vaulted study with arched window

- A well-equipped kitchen opens to the bayed breakfast room and the vaulted hearth room

- The second floor enjoys a spacious media room along with three huge bedrooms

- 4 bedrooms, 3 1/2 baths, 3-car side entry garage

- Walk-out basement foundation

Second Floor
1,648 sq. ft.

First Floor
2,817 sq. ft.

Elegant Tudor Is Ideal For A Growing Family

- 3,641 total square feet of living area

- Secluded family room includes a large fireplace, patio sliding doors and easy access to the kitchen and dining room

- The front of the home consists of a formal living room and an adjacent library for quiet time

- Focal point of the second floor is a large central sitting room that is perfect as a children's play area or an office

- Covered front porch adds charm to the design

- 5 bedrooms, 4 baths, 3-car side entry garage

- Basement foundation

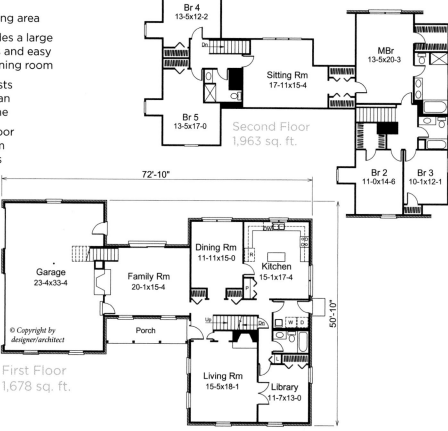

Br 4
13-5x12-2

MBr
13-5x20-3

Sitting Rm
17-11x15-4

Br 5
13-5x17-0

Second Floor
1,963 sq. ft.

Br 2
11-0x14-6

Br 3
10-1x12-1

72'-10"

Garage
23-4x33-4

Family Rm
20-1x15-4

Dining Rm
11-11x15-0

Kitchen
15-1x17-4

Porch

© Copyright by
designer/architect

Living Rm
15-5x18-1

Library
11-7x13-0

50'-10"

First Floor
1,678 sq. ft.

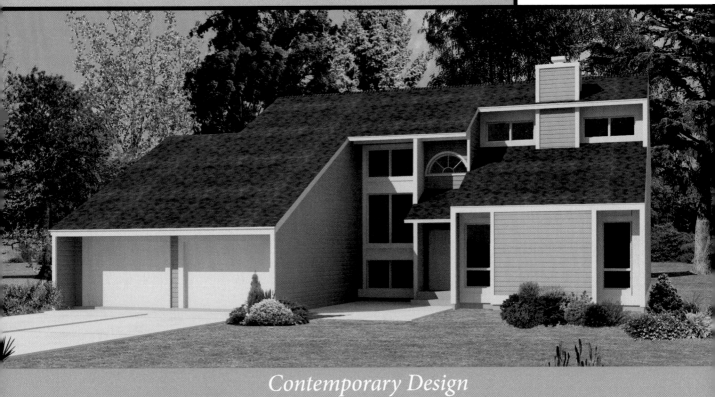

Contemporary Design

- 2,510 total square feet of living area
- Energy efficient home with 2" x 6" exterior walls
- Both formal and informal living spaces are graced with stylish fireplaces
- Enjoy the large deck and sunroom located off the dining room
- All of the bedrooms are located on the second floor, including the master suite complete with a private balcony
- 3 bedrooms, 2 1/2 baths, 2-car garage
- Basement foundation

Second Floor
1,086 sq. ft.

First Floor
1,424 sq. ft.

Charming Covered Front Porch

- 2,547 total square feet of living area
- Energy efficient home with 2" x 6" exterior walls
- Second floor makes economical use of area above garage allowing for three bedrooms and a study/fourth bedroom
- First floor study is ideal for a home office
- Large pantry is located in the efficient kitchen
- 3 bedrooms, 2 1/2 baths, 2-car garage
- Basement foundation

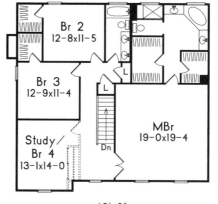

Second Floor
1,464 sq. ft.

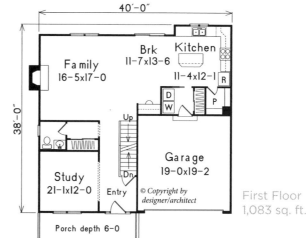

First Floor
1,083 sq. ft.

Vaulted Ceiling In Living Room Adds Spaciousness

- 2,838 total square feet of living area
- Energy efficient home with 2" x 6" exterior walls
- 10' ceilings throughout the first floor
- Dining room is enhanced with large corner bay windows
- Master bath boasts a double-bowl vanity and an oversized tub
- Kitchen features an island and double sink which overlooks the dinette and family room
- 4 bedrooms, 3 baths, 3-car garage
- Basement foundation

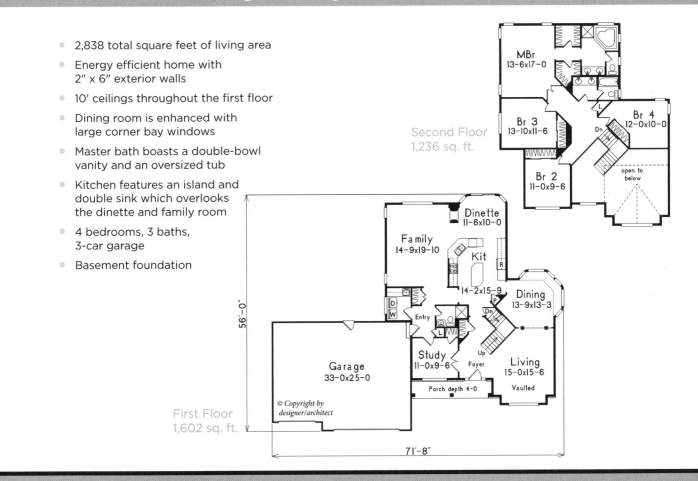

Second Floor
1,236 sq. ft.

First Floor
1,602 sq. ft.

Vaulted Two-Story Great Room

- 2,205 total square feet of living area

- The master bedroom enjoys a private first floor location along with a private bath and walk-in closet

- A flexible loft space can be found on the second floor perfect for a home office or children's play area

- The functional kitchen offers an eating bar and a corner walk-in pantry for added storage space

- 3 bedrooms, 2 1/2 baths, 2-car side entry garage

- Basement foundation

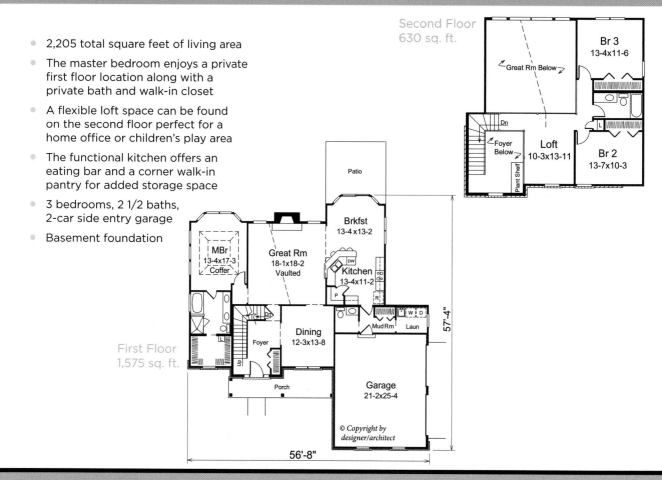

Stylish Two-Story Provides Room For Large Family

- 2,730 total square feet of living area
- Spacious kitchen features an island and generous walk-in pantry
- Covered deck offers a private retreat to the outdoors
- Large master bedroom has a bath with a corner whirlpool tub, separate shower and double walk-in closets
- Oversized laundry room is conveniently located off the kitchen
- 4 bedrooms, 2 1/2 baths, 3-car side entry garage with storage area
- Basement foundation

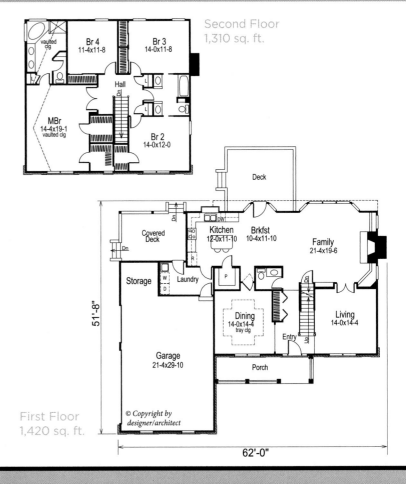

Second Floor
1,310 sq. ft.

Br 4
11-4x11-8

Br 3
14-0x11-8

vaulted clg

Hall

MBr
14-4x19-1
vaulted clg

Br 2
14-0x12-0

Deck

Covered Deck

Kitchen
12-0x11-10

Brkfst
10-4x11-10

Family
21-4x19-6

Storage

Laundry

Dining
14-0x14-4
tray clg

Living
14-0x14-4

Garage
21-4x29-10

Entry

Porch

51'-8"

62'-0"

© Copyright by designer/architect

First Floor
1,420 sq. ft.

Double Bay Windows Provide Sweeping View

- 2,498 total square feet of living area
- Main rooms of this Colonial style home are oriented to the rear of the house
- Bay windows can be found in the dining room, breakfast nook, master bedroom and bath
- Oversized laundry and pantry are conveniently located
- Luxurious master bath and dressing area
- Bonus room above the garage, which is included in the square footage, has many possibilities and offers a generous storage area
- 3 bedrooms, 2 1/2 baths, 2-car garage
- Crawl space foundation

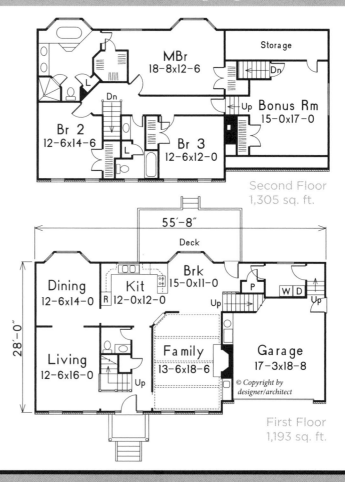

Storage

MBr
18-8x12-6

Bonus Rm
15-0x17-0

Br 2
12-6x14-6

Br 3
12-6x12-0

Second Floor
1,305 sq. ft.

55'-8"

Deck

Dining
12-6x14-0

Kit
12-0x12-0

Brk
15-0x11-0

P

W D

28'-0"

Living
12-6x16-0

Family
13-6x18-6

Garage
17-3x18-8

© Copyright by
designer/architect

First Floor
1,193 sq. ft.

Plan #542-006D-0004 • Price Code C

Blends Open And Private Living Areas

- 1,996 total square feet of living area
- Dining area features an octagon-shaped coffered ceiling and built-in china cabinet
- Both the master bath and second floor bath have cheerful skylights
- Family room includes a wet bar and fireplace flanked by attractive quarter round windows
- 9' ceilings can be found throughout the first floor with plant shelving in the foyer and dining area
- 3 bedrooms, 2 1/2 baths, 2-car side entry garage
- Basement foundation, drawings also include crawl space and slab foundations

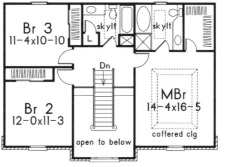

Br 3
11-4x10-10

Br 2
12-0x11-3

Dn

open to below

MBr
14-4x16-5
coffered clg

Second Floor
859 sq. ft.

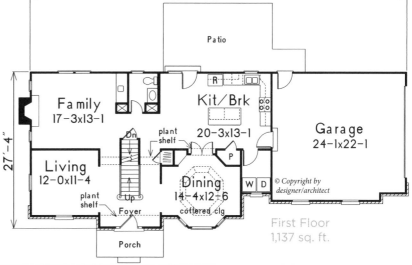

68'-4"

Patio

27'-4"

Family
17-3x13-1

Kit/Brk
20-3x13-1

Garage
24-1x22-1

Living
12-0x11-4

plant shelf

Dn

plant shelf

Dining
14-4x12-6
coffered clg

W D

© Copyright by
designer/architect

Foyer

Up

Porch

First Floor
1,137 sq. ft.

Spectacular Curb Appeal

- 2,484 total square feet of living area
- Columns and an arched opening frame the kitchen from the great room, and a box-bay window expands the breakfast area
- A triple sliding glass door introduces an abundance of light and invites the activities to continue to the rear covered porch
- A secondary bedroom with a private bath makes a wonderful guest room
- 4 bedrooms, 3 1/2 baths, 2-car side entry garage
- Basement foundation

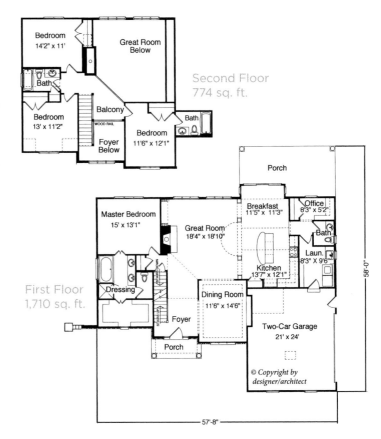

Second Floor
774 sq. ft.

Bedroom
14'2" x 11'

Great Room
Below

Bath

Bedroom
13' x 11'2"

Balcony

WOOD RAIL

Foyer
Below

Bath

Bedroom
11'6" x 12'1"

First Floor
1,710 sq. ft.

Master Bedroom
15 x 13'1"

Dressing

Great Room
18'4" x 18'10"

Breakfast
11'5" x 11'3"

Office
8'3" x 5'2"

Bath

Kitchen
13'7" x 12'1"

Laun.
8'3" X 9'6"

Foyer

Dining Room
11'6" x 14'6"

Porch

Two-Car Garage
21' x 24'

Porch

© Copyright by
designer/architect

58'-0"

57'-8"

Lovely Sunroom

- 3,376 total square feet of living area
- The entry draws guests in with the circular staircase and 18' vaulted ceiling
- Triple 8' high French doors provide a view of the backyard from the famly room
- Bedrooms #3 and #4 share a Jack and Jill bath
- 4 bedrooms, 3 1/2 baths, 2-car side entry garage
- Walk-out basement foundation

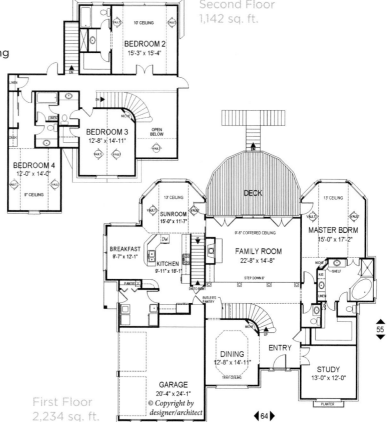

Second Floor
1,142 sq. ft.

BEDROOM 2
15'-3" x 15'-4"

BEDROOM 3
12'-8" x 14'-11"

BEDROOM 4
12'-0" x 14'-0"

DECK

SUNROOM
15'-0" x 11'-7"

FAMILY ROOM
22'-8" x 14'-8"

MASTER BDRM
15'-0" x 17'-2"

BREAKFAST
9'-7" x 12'-1"

KITCHEN
9'-11" x 18'-1"

DINING
12'-8" x 14'-11"

ENTRY

STUDY
13'-0" x 12'-0"

GARAGE
20'-4" x 24'-1"

© Copyright by designer/architect

First Floor
2,234 sq. ft.

Attractive Facade And Good Planning

- 2,372 total square feet of living area

- Spacious living room features an opening to the entry flanked by bookshelves

- Sunken family room boasts an impressive fireplace and large window wall

- Well-appointed kitchen includes a snack counter

- Second floor bedrooms combine extravagant room sizes with lots of walk-in closets

- 4 bedrooms, 2 1/2 baths, 2-car garage

- Basement foundation, drawings also include crawl space and slab foundations

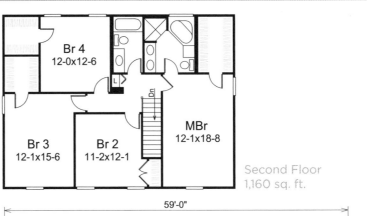

Br 4
12-0x12-6

MBr
12-1x18-8

Br 3
12-1x15-6

Br 2
11-2x12-1

Second Floor
1,160 sq. ft.

59'-0"

Dining Rm
10-8x12-6

Kit
9-0x
12-6

Brkfst
10-6x12-6

Family Rm
18-7x12-6

Living Rm
18-5x14-6

Entry

Utility

Garage
21-4x23-4

Stoop

36'-10"

First Floor
1,212 sq. ft.

© Copyright by
designer/architect

Intricate Details Make This Home Interesting

- 2,685 total square feet of living area
- Vaulted great room has a large fireplace and a wet bar
- Sunny breakfast area has a large bay window and access outdoors
- All secondary bedrooms are on the second floor for privacy
- 4 bedrooms, 3 1/2 baths, 2-car side entry garage
- Partial basement/crawl space foundation

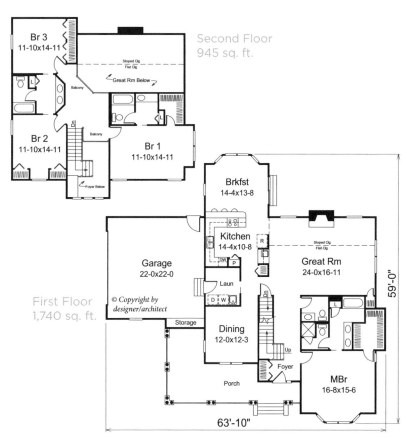

Second Floor
945 sq. ft.

Br 3
11-10x14-11

Sloped Clg
Flat Clg

Great Rm Below

Balcony

Br 2
11-10x14-11

Balcony

Dn

Br 1
11-10x14-11

Foyer Below

First Floor
1,740 sq. ft.

© Copyright by
designer/architect

Brkfst
14-4x13-8

Kitchen
14-4x10-8

Garage
22-0x22-0

Great Rm
24-0x16-11

Sloped Clg
Flat Clg

Laun

Storage

Dining
12-0x12-3

Up

Foyer

MBr
16-8x15-6

Porch

59'-0"

63'-10"

Spacious One-Story With French Country Flavor

- 2,695 total square feet of living area

- A grand-scale great room features a fireplace with flanking shelves, handsome entry foyer with staircase and opens to a large kitchen and breakfast room

- Roomy master bedroom has a bay window, huge walk-in closet and bath

- Bedrooms #2 and #3 are generously oversized with walk-in closets and a Jack and Jill style bath

- 2" x 6" exterior walls available, please order plan #542-007E-0117

- 3 bedrooms, 2 1/2 baths, 2-car side entry garage

- Basement foundation

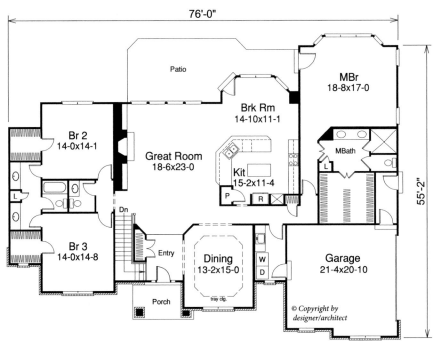

Picture Perfect For A Country Setting

- 2,967 total square feet of living area
- The charming exterior is graced with a country porch and multiple arched projected box windows
- Dining area is oversized and adjoins a fully equipped kitchen with walk-in pantry
- Two bay windows light up the enormous informal living spaces to the rear
- 4 bedrooms, 3 1/2 baths, 3-car side entry garage
- Basement foundation

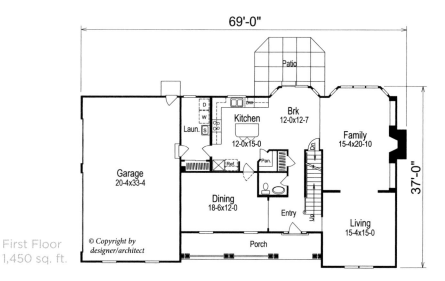

Second Floor
1,517 sq. ft.

First Floor
1,450 sq. ft.

© Copyright by
designer/architect

Dignified Ranch Exterior

- 2,024 total square feet of living area
- Lovely covered porch provides weather protection
- Living and dining rooms combine and include double French doors to the adjoining deck
- Beautiful three-season porch features an abundance of windows
- 3 bedrooms, 2 baths, 2-car garage
- Basement foundation

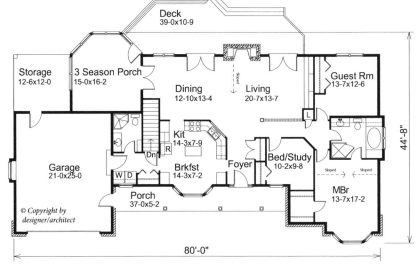

Great Traffic Flow On Both Floors

- 2,461 total square feet of living area
- Unique corner tub, double vanities and walk-in closet enhance the large master bedroom
- Fireplace provides focus in the spacious family room
- Centrally located half bath on the first floor for guests
- 4 bedrooms, 2 1/2 baths, 2-car garage
- Basement foundation, drawings also include slab and crawl space foundations

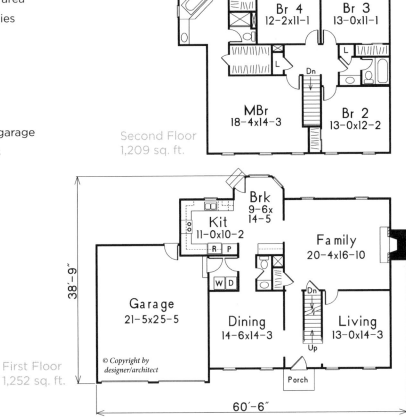

Second Floor
1,209 sq. ft.

First Floor
1,252 sq. ft.

Luxurious Living Embraces The Outdoors

- 2,773 total square feet of living area
- Exposed roof rafters illuminate the window seat in the huge living room that also features built-in bookshelves, a fireplace and a cathedral ceiling
- Kitchen with cooktop island has breakfast bar opening to the activity area with a vaulted ceiling
- Laundry room, bedroom # 3 and library with built-in bookshelves occupy the left portion of the home
- Master bedroom features a double-vanity bath with two walk-in closets and double sliding glass doors leading to the deck
- 3 bedrooms, 3 baths, 2-car side entry garage
- Partial basement/crawl space foundation, drawings also include slab foundation

Country Home Designed For Entertaining

- 2,873 total square feet of living area

- A stately foyer leads into a two-story atrium with winding stairs featuring a plant shelf with clerestory windows and vaulted ceiling above

- The hearth and breakfast rooms offer a 31' vista with adjacent study or private fourth bedroom boasting its own bath and walk-in closet, ideal for guests or live-in mother-in-law

- The large covered rear patio area includes a vaulted ceiling with skylights, walk-in wet bar with serving counter and sauna room, perfect for entertaining

- 4 bedrooms, 3 1/2 baths, 2-car side entry garage

- Basement foundation

Second Floor
1,149 sq. ft.

MBr
18-0x13-0

Br 2
13-0x12-0

Atrium
vaulted

Br 3
13-0x13-1

Hall

Attic

plant shelf
w/clerestory
windows above

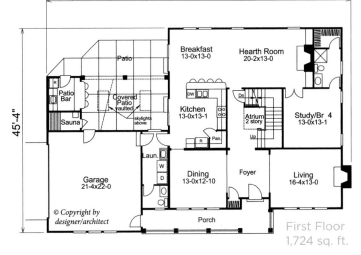

70'-4"

45'-4"

Patio

Breakfast
13-0x13-0

Hearth Room
20-2x13-0

Patio Bar

Covered Patio
vaulted

skylights above

Sauna

Kitchen
13-0x13-1

Atrium
2 story

Study/Br 4
13-0x13-1

Pan.

Up

Laun.

W
D

Dining
13-0x12-10

Foyer

Living
16-4x13-0

Garage
21-4x22-0

© Copyright by
designer/architect

Porch

First Floor
1,724 sq. ft.

Wrap-Around Front Country Porch

- 2,665 total square feet of living area
- 9' ceilings on the first floor
- Spacious kitchen features many cabinets, a center island cooktop and bayed breakfast area adjacent to the laundry room
- Second floor bedrooms boast walk-in closets, dressing areas and share a bath
- Twin French doors and fireplace grace the living room
- 4 bedrooms, 3 baths, 2-car rear entry garage
- Slab foundation, drawings also include crawl space foundation

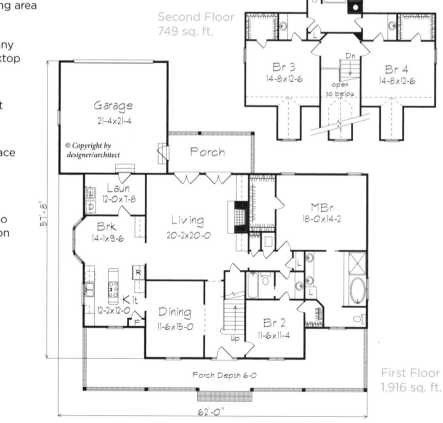

Second Floor 749 sq. ft.

Br 3 14-8x12-6

Br 4 14-8x12-6

open to below

Dn

Garage 21-4x21-4

© Copyright by designer/architect

Porch

Laun 12-0x7-8

Brk 14-1x9-6

Living 20-2x20-0

MBr 18-0x14-2

Kit 12-2x12-0

Dining 11-6x15-0

Br 2 11-6x11-4

Up

51'-8"

Porch Depth 6-0

62'-0"

First Floor 1,916 sq. ft.

LOWE'S LEGACY SERIES

Clean, Practical Colonial

- 2,328 total square feet of living area
- Formal living and dining rooms feature floor-to-ceiling windows
- Kitchen with island counter and pantry makes cooking a delight
- Expansive master bedroom has luxury bath with double vanity and walk-in closet
- 4 bedrooms, 2 1/2 baths, 2-car garage
- Basement foundation, drawings also include slab and crawl space foundations

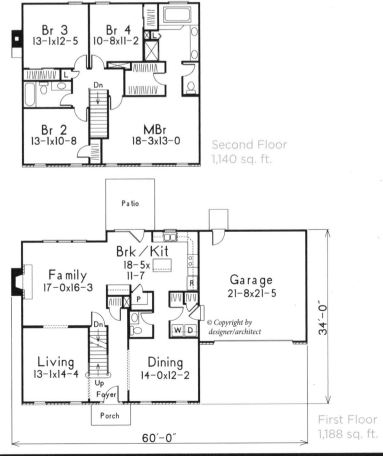

Br 3
13-1x12-5

Br 4
10-8x11-2

Br 2
13-1x10-8

Dn

MBr
18-3x13-0

Second Floor
1,140 sq. ft.

Patio

Family
17-0x16-3

Brk/Kit
18-5x
11-7

Garage
21-8x21-5

R

Dn

P

W D

© Copyright by designer/architect

Living
13-1x14-4

Dining
14-0x12-2

Up
Foyer

Porch

34'-0"

60'-0"

First Floor
1,188 sq. ft.

Plan #542-048D-0008 • Price Code C

Stately Covered Front Entry

- 2,089 total square feet of living area
- Family room features a fireplace, built-in bookshelves and triple sliders opening to the covered patio
- The kitchen overlooks the family room and features a pantry and desk
- Separated from the three secondary bedrooms, the master bedroom becomes a quiet retreat with patio access
- Master bedroom features an oversized bath with walk-in closet and corner tub
- 4 bedrooms, 3 baths, 2-car garage
- Slab foundation

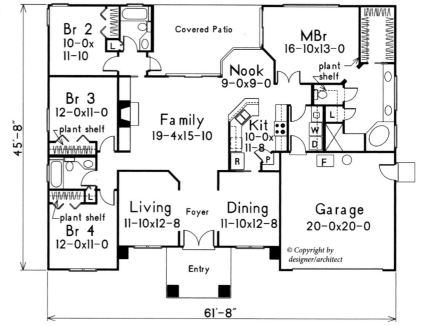

Magnificent Great Room In A Classic Tudor

- 2,541 total square feet of living area

- The sophisticated exterior is complimented by traditional Old English detail including stucco, stone, wood trim and decorative lightning rods atop multiple gables

- An expansive porch leads to the foyer and into enormous vaulted living areas with a handcrafted staircase and upper dining overlook

- The lower level great room features a two-story vaulted ceiling with optional decorative trusses, a 24' high stone fireplace, game room, its own kitchen and bar, 9' wide glass doors to patio and lots of windows

- Future movie theater or fourth bedroom with bath and walk-in closet available on the lower level

- The bedroom wing, with two secondary bedrooms and bath, offers a master bedroom with luxury bath, two walk-in closets, double entry doors and vaulted ceiling

- 4 bedrooms, 3 baths, 2-car garage

- Walk-out basement foundation

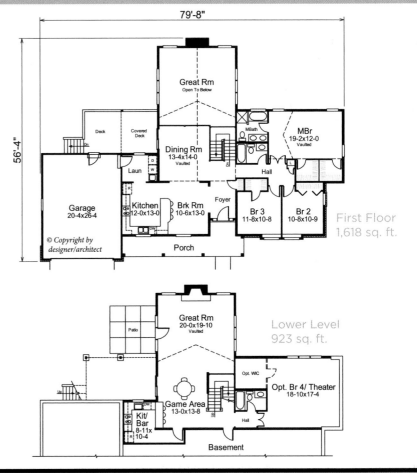

First Floor
1,618 sq. ft.

Lower Level
923 sq. ft.

© Copyright by designer/architect

Stately Country Home For The "Spacious Age"

- 2,727 total square feet of living area

- Wrap-around porch and large entry create an impressive entrance

- A state-of-the-art vaulted kitchen has a walk-in pantry and is open to the breakfast area and adjoining screen-in-porch

- A walk-in wet bar, fireplace, bay window and deck access are features of the family room

- Vaulted master bedroom enjoys a luxurious bath with skylight and an enormous 13' deep walk-in closet

- 4 bedrooms, 2 1/2 baths, 2-car side entry garage

- Walk-out basement foundation

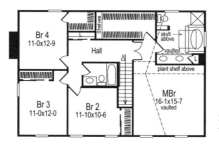

Second Floor
1,204 sq. ft.

First Floor
1,523 sq. ft.

© Copyright by designer/architect

Private Apartment Within A Home

- 3,346 total square feet of living area
- The kitchen is open to the informal dining and breakfast areas with views of the rear covered walkway and patio featuring a walk-in bar and sauna room
- A second covered patio, luxury bath, walk-in closet and bay window are some of the amenities of the first floor master bedroom
- In addition to the three generously-sized bedrooms on the second floor, a private apartment is located to the rear of the home, truly ideal for guests, in-laws, students or a studio
- 5 bedrooms, 4 full baths, 2 half baths, 2-car side entry garage
- Walk-out basement foundation

Lower Level
380 sq. ft.

Second Floor
1,170 sq. ft.

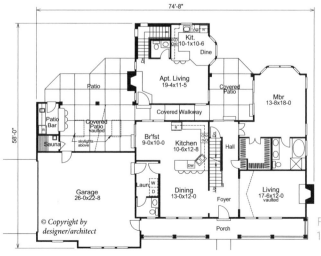

First Floor
1,796 sq. ft.

Plan #542-007D-0058 • Price Code G

A Spectacular Showplace

- 4,863 total square feet of living area
- Brightly lit entry connects to the great room with balcony and massive bay-shaped atrium
- Kitchen has island/snack bar, walk-in pantry, computer area and an atrium overlook
- Master bedroom has a sitting area, walk-in closets, atrium overlook and luxury bath with private courtyard
- Family room/atrium, home theater area with wet bar, game room and guest bedroom comprise the lower level
- 4 bedrooms, 3 1/2 baths, 3-car side entry garage
- Walk-out basement foundation

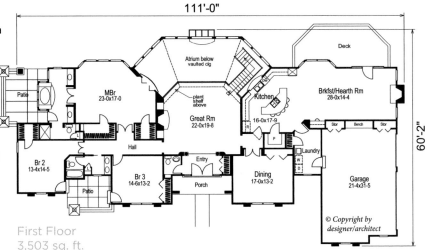

First Floor
3,503 sq. ft.

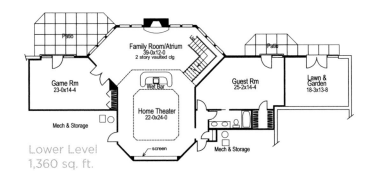

Lower Level
1,360 sq. ft.

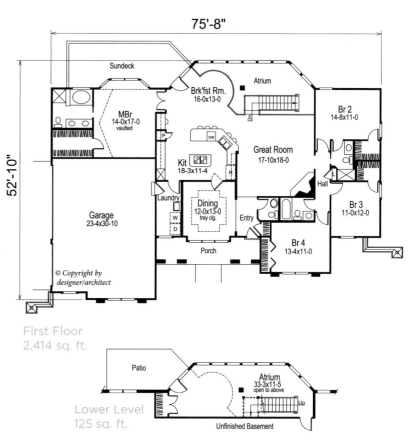

Tantalizing Atrium Home

- 2,539 total square feet of living area

- Stunning exterior creates value

- The large great room, breakfast room/balcony and spacious kitchen all enjoy dazzling views through the two-story window wall of the atrium bay

- The dining room features a handsome tray ceiling and three patio doors to the front porch designed to be fixed or operable

- The secluded master bedroom enjoys a double-door entry, a bay window overlooking the sundeck, a huge walk-in closet and a lavish bath

- 4 bedrooms, 3 1/2 baths, 3-car side entry garage

- Walk-out basement foundation

75'-8"

52'-10"

Sundeck

Atrium

Brk'fst Rm.
16-0x13-0

MBr
14-0x17-0
vaulted

Br 2
14-8x11-0

Kit
18-3x11-4

Great Room
17-10x18-0

Garage
23-4x30-10

Laundry

Dining
12-0x13-0
tray clg.

Hall

Br 3
11-0x12-0

Entry

W
D

Br 4
13-4x11-0

Porch

© *Copyright by designer/architect*

First Floor
2,414 sq. ft.

Patio

Atrium
33-3x11-5
open to above

Lower Level
125 sq. ft.

Up

Unfinished Basement

Fashionable Family Home

- 2,021 total square feet of living area

- A corner garden tub in the private master bath becomes the ultimate retreat from the stresses of everyday life

- A large eating area extends off the kitchen featuring a center island and access to the covered porch with outdoor kitchen

- A media/hobby room can be found through double doors in the large great room

- The unfinished bonus room has an additional 354 square feet of living area

- 3 bedrooms, 2 1/2 baths, 2-car side entry garage

- Basement foundation, drawings also include slab and crawl space foundations

Optional
Second Floor

Unfinished
Bonus
Room
14-0 x 23-6
(Clear)
8-0 Clg. Ht.

Covered Porch
23-0 x 8-0

Patio

M. Bath
15-4 x 9-6

Master
Bedroom
14-0 x 15-6

Kitchen
11-6 x 15-6

Eating
11-2 x 15-6

Bedroom 2
13-4 x 11-6

Clos.
7-6 x 5-8

Clos.
7-6 x 5-8

Hall
Bath

Stor.
8-5 x 7-4

Utility
8-3 x 7-4

Entry

Half
Bath

Great Room
22-8 x 15-6
(Clear)

Media/
Hobby
8-0 x 7-10

Bedroom 3
13-4 x 11-6

Covered Porch
23-0 x 5-0

2 Car Garage
23-4 x 23-6

© Copyright by
designer/architect

Width: 69'-0"
Depth: 63'-10"

First Floor
2,021 sq. ft.

Elaborate Home Excels In Design

- 4,522 total square feet of living area
- Large living room with cathedral ceiling views the front terrace
- The kitchen, a cheery breakfast area and the huge family room combine creating an exciting space
- First floor master bedroom features a bath that defines luxury
- A second staircase serves the second floor's three bedrooms and mammoth storage area which is included in the total square footage
- 4 bedrooms, 3 full baths, 2 half baths, 2-car garage
- Partial basement/crawl space foundation

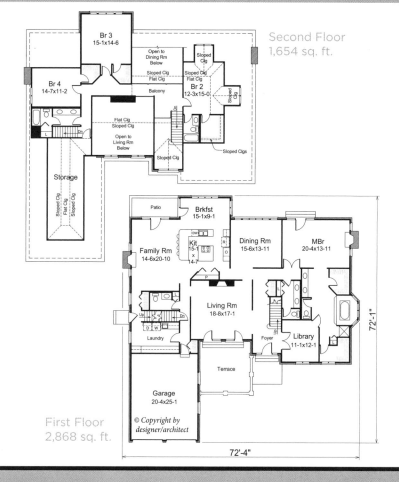

Second Floor
1,654 sq. ft.

First Floor
2,868 sq. ft.

© Copyright by
designer/architect

Corner Quoins Add Elegance To Exterior

- 2,760 total square feet of living area
- Both secondary bedrooms on the second floor have their own full baths and large activity areas
- The screened porch off the family room offers a place for outdoor relaxation
- A box-bay window adds charm and character to guest bedroom #4
- 4 bedrooms, 4 baths, 3 1/2-car side entry garage
- Basement foundation

Second Floor
1,460 sq. ft.

First Floor
1,300 sq. ft.

Wheelchair Friendly And Energy Efficient

- 2,884 total square feet of living area

- A superb blend of brick, stone, board and batten shutters and diamond window grilles create this stylish English Tudor

- Designed for energy efficiency, this home includes R68 ceiling insulation, 2x6 wall construction with R33 insulated vinyl siding, triple-glazed insulated wood windows and doors and a cedar shake roof

- All halls, doorways and rooms are designed for wheelchair access

- The great room enjoys a fireplace with flanking shelves, space for an optional elevator, and is open to a bright atrium on the lower level with an additional 100 square feet

- 3 bedrooms, 2 1/2 baths, 2-car side entry garage

- Walk-out basement foundation

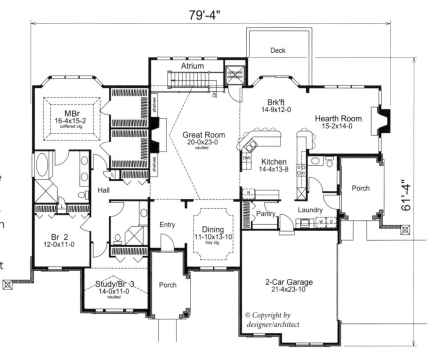

Old English Luxury

- 6,088 total square feet of living area

- The two-story foyer invites you into the grand scale great room featuring a two-story stone fireplace, flanking bookshelves and window wall

- Amenities galore are found in the huge kitchen including a 9' island with seating, octagonal breakfast area, vaulted hearth room with fireplace and covered porch

- The master bedroom offers a bay window, coffered ceiling and colossal bath with sauna, whirlpool tub and two enormous walk-in closets

- The garage with large storage room includes an adjacent office with private entrance, half bath and patio

- Three bedrooms, each with their own bath and walk-in closet, a dramatic balcony overlooking the great room and private staircase to the kitchen are features of the second floor

- 4 bedrooms, 4 full baths, 2 half baths, 5-car side entry garage

- Basement foundation

Attractive Bay Kitchen

- 2,716 total square feet of living area
- 9' ceilings throughout the first floor
- All bedrooms boast walk-in closets
- Great room and hearth room share a see-through fireplace
- Balcony overlooks the large great room
- 4 bedrooms, 4 1/2 baths, 2-car side entry garage
- Basement foundation

Second Floor
962 sq. ft.

First Floor
1,754 sq. ft.

© Copyright by designer/architect

Prestigious And Family Oriented

- 3,420 total square feet of living area

- Hip roofs, elliptical windows and brick facade with quoins emphasize stylish sophisticated living

- Grand foyer has flared staircase in addition to secondary staircase from the kitchen

- Enormous kitchen features a cooktop island, walk-in pantry, angled breakfast bar and computer desk

- Splendid gallery connects family room and wet bar with vaulted hearth room

- Master bedroom has a coffered ceiling, double walk-in closets and a lavish bath

- 4 bedrooms, 3 1/2 baths, 3-car rear entry garage

- Walk-out basement foundation

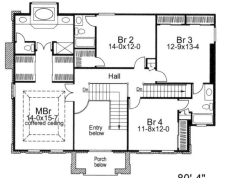

Second Floor
1,526 sq. ft.

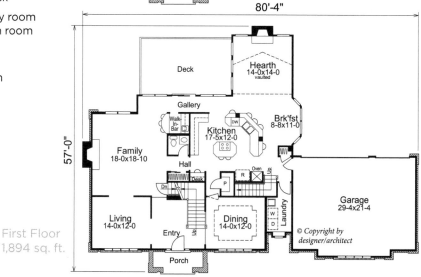

First Floor
1,894 sq. ft.

© Copyright by designer/architect

Carefully Designed For Energy Efficiency

- 2,882 total square feet of living area
- Designed for north orientation, the garage roof deflects winds, the insulated garage acts as a thermal barrier to the home's finished spaces, and triple-glazed insulated wood windows and doors are used in major glass areas facing south with no windows in north walls
- 2" x 6" walls with multiple insulating materials create an approximate value of R34 with R70 in the attic
- The basement has insulated walls inside and out and a natural cooling system created by a 40' long buried pipe that provides a constant 55-degree earth temperature
- The shake roof provides over three times the insulating value of asphalt shingles
- 3 bedrooms, 3 1/2 baths, 3-car garage with shop
- Basement foundation

Second Floor
902 sq. ft.

Lower Level
937 sq. ft.

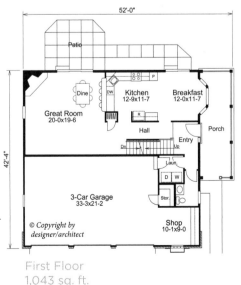

First Floor
1,043 sq. ft.

Attractive Entry Created By Full-Length Porch

- 2,357 total square feet of living area

- 9' ceilings on the first floor

- Secluded master bedroom includes a private bath with double walk-in closets and vanity

- Balcony overlooks living room with large fireplace

- The future game room on the second floor has an additional 303 square feet of living area

- 4 bedrooms, 3 1/2 baths, 2-car side entry garage

- Slab foundation, drawings also include crawl space foundation

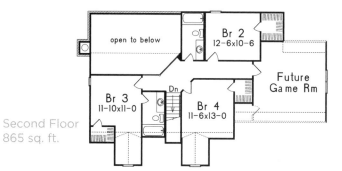

Second Floor
865 sq. ft.

Br 2
12-6x10-6

open to below

Future
Game Rm

Br 3
11-10x11-0

Dn

Br 4
11-6x13-0

66'-0"

Covered
Porch

Brk
10-0x9-6

W D

Storage

Living
21-0x15-6

Kit
12-0x13-0

Garage
20-7x21-6

raised ceiling

34'-2"

MBr
13-0x17-8

Dining
12-0x12-8

*© Copyright by
designer/architect*

First Floor
1,492 sq. ft.

Porch

LOWE'S
LEGACY
SERIES

Beauty And Function

- 4,597 total square feet of living area

- A two-story palladian entrance welcomes you to a spacious foyer with second floor balcony overlook

- The enormous great room with fireplace is convenient to the nearby study with window seat

- A state-of-the-art kitchen offers corner windows at the sink, an island snack bar, large walk-in pantry and adjoins the laundry area with a second pantry

- The master bedroom has a stylish bath and over 200 square feet of walk-in closet space

- 4 bedrooms, 4 1/2 baths, 3-car side entry garage

- Basement foundation

Second Floor
2,202 sq. ft.

MBr 18-2x16-4 vaulted
Plant shelf above
Br 2 13-2x12-5
Br 3 13-8x13-0
Seat
Hall
Balcony
Br 4 14-0x12-1
Foyer Below
Playroom 13-8x18-8
Porch Below

66'-4"
60'-4"

Patio
Kitchen 15-4x14-8
Brk'ft Rm 15-6x19-3
Great Rm 20-0x21-7
Study 13-8x14-8
Seat
Laundry
Mud Rm
Hall
Up
Hall
Dining 14-0x16-6 tray clg.
Foyer 2 story
Living Rm 13-8x16-6
Garage 21-4x29-4
Porch

© Copyright by designer/architect

First Floor
2,395 sq. ft.

Formal Home, Enhanced By Huge Foyer

- 3,200 total square feet of living area
- Two-story foyer and graceful curved stairway are flanked by separate living and dining rooms
- Master bedroom suite on the second floor has a double-door entry, fireplace and a bath with a step-up tub built into the bay window
- 4 bedrooms, 2 1/2 baths, 2-car side entry garage
- Basement foundation

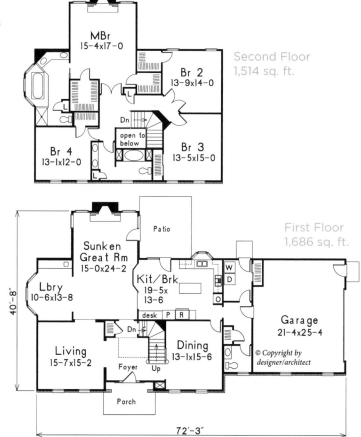

Second Floor
1,514 sq. ft.

MBr
15-4x17-0

Br 2
13-9x14-0

Br 4
13-1x12-0

Br 3
13-5x15-0

Dn

open to below

First Floor
1,686 sq. ft.

Patio

Sunken Great Rm
15-0x24-2

Kit/Brk
19-5x 13-6

Lbry
10-6x13-8

desk P R

Dn

Living
15-7x15-2

Dining
13-1x15-6

Foyer

Up

Garage
21-4x25-4

W D

© Copyright by designer/architect

Porch

40'-8"

72'-3"

Inviting Craftsman Ranch

- 3,520 total square feet of living area
- From the welcoming front porch to the screened porch and deck, this home provides dramatic spaces, luxurious appointments, and spacious living areas
- The sunny breakfast room has a conveniently located laundry closet
- Loaded with amenities such as a tray ceiling, the dramatic master suite features a sitting area, deluxe bath, and a "his and hers" walk-in closets and has direct access to the screened porch
- The optional second floor has an additional 1,224 square feet of living area
- 4 bedrooms, 4 baths, 2-car side entry garage
- Walk-out basement foundation

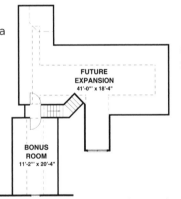

Optional Second Floor

FUTURE EXPANSION 41'-0" x 18'-4"

BONUS ROOM 11'-2" x 20'-4"

Lower Level 1,820 sq. ft.

First Floor 1,700 sq. ft.

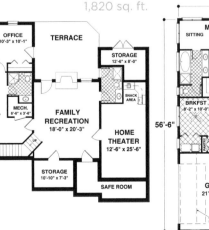

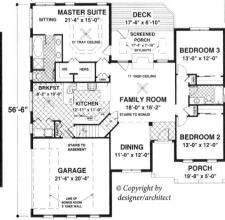

© Copyright by designer/architect

Large Bedrooms With An Abundance Of Closets

- 3,072 total square feet of living area
- The grand, two-story foyer features a view of the impressive circular staircase
- The formal living and dining rooms combine, and offer stunning bow windows and a pass-through to the kitchen
- A handsome fireplace warms the expansive family room that also includes a bay window and opens to the breakfast area
- 4 bedrooms, 2 full baths, 3 half baths, 2-car side entry garage
- Partial walk-out basement/crawl space foundation, drawings also include slab foundation

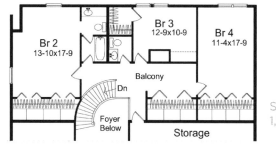

Second Floor
1,152 sq. ft.

Br 2
13-10x17-9

Br 3
12-9x10-9

Br 4
11-4x17-9

Balcony

Dn

Foyer Below

Storage

74'-0"

40'-0"

First Floor
1,920 sq. ft.

MBr
13-10x12-0

Family
15-3x13-11

Brkfst
14-0x9-5

Mud Rm.

Lndry
9-10x8-6

Util. F

Kit
16-10x9-1

R

Office/Study
10-4x12-4

Dn

Up

Foyer

Living
12-5x12-2

Dining
12-7x12-2

Garage
23-8x26-2

Porch

© Copyright by designer/architect

LOWE'S
LEGACY
SERIES

Two-Story Atrium For Great Views

- 2,724 total square feet of living area

- Elegant entry foyer leads to the second floor balcony overlook of the vaulted two-story atrium

- Spacious kitchen features an island breakfast bar, walk-in pantry, bayed breakfast area and adjoining screened porch

- Two large second floor bedrooms and stair balconies overlook a sun-drenched two-story vaulted atrium

- 4 bedrooms, 3 1/2 baths, 2-car side entry garage

- Basement foundation

Second Floor
861 sq. ft.

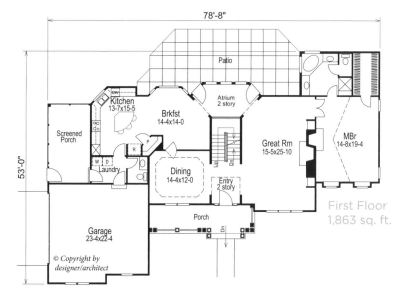

First Floor
1,863 sq. ft.

Dramatic And Exciting Interior

- 3,882 total square feet of living area

- The stately foyer is two stories tall with two guest closets and balcony overlook

- A colossal-sized family room enjoys a fireplace with log bin and walk-around wet bar

- A large first floor study provides a secluded retreat

- Second floor balcony views family room and foyer below

- 4 bedrooms, 3 baths, 3-car side entry garage

- Basement foundation

Second Floor
1,632 sq. ft.

MBr
15-0x17-1

Open to Family Rm Below

Balcony

Br 1
13-1x12-5

Br 2
12-0x11-5

Open to Foyer Below

Br 3
15-0x16-6

First Floor
2,250 sq. ft.

50'-4"

78'-5"

Storage

Laundry

Brkfst
16-8x10-0

Kitchen
16-0x15-6

Family Rm
21-4x26-4

Bar

Garage
23-4x30-0

Study
12-0x15-2

Dining Rm
13-1x15-6

Foyer

Living Rm
15-0x17-3

© Copyright by designer/architect

Active Living Areas Throughout

- 3,808 total square feet of living area
- Cozy hearth room shares a fireplace with the great room
- See-through fireplace connects gathering areas
- Master bath features stylish angled glass block walls that frame the private toilet and large shower
- 3 bedrooms, 3 baths, 2-car garage
- Walk-out basement foundation

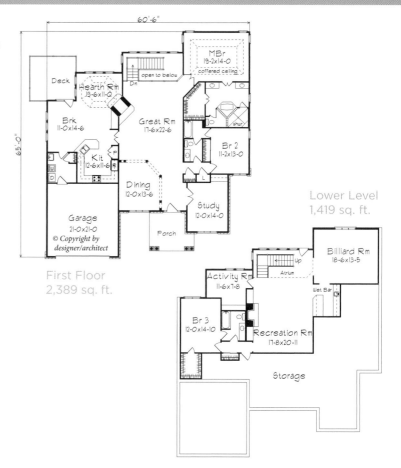

First Floor
2,389 sq. ft.

Lower Level
1,419 sq. ft.

Large Porch And Balcony Create Impressive Exterior

- 2,352 total square feet of living area
- Energy efficient home with 2" x 6" exterior walls
- Separate family and living rooms for casual and formal entertaining
- Master bedroom with private dressing area and bath
- Bedrooms are located on the second floor for privacy
- 4 bedrooms, 2 1/2 baths, 2-car rear entry garage
- Crawl space foundation, drawings also include basement and slab foundations

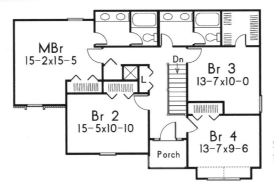

MBr
15-2x15-5

Br 2
15-5x10-10

Dn

Br 3
13-7x10-0

Br 4
13-7x9-6

Porch

Second Floor
1,182 sq. ft.

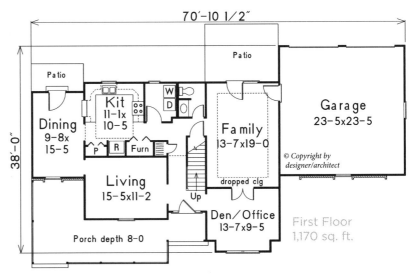

70'-10 1/2"

Patio

Patio

Patio

Kit
11-1x
10-5

W
D

Dining
9-8x
15-5

Garage
23-5x23-5

Family
13-7x19-0

P R Furn

38'-0"

Living
15-5x11-2

Up

dropped clg

© Copyright by
designer/architect

Den/Office
13-7x9-5

Porch depth 8-0

First Floor
1,170 sq. ft.

LOWE'S
LEGACY
SERIES

Great Looks Accentuated By Elliptical Brick Arches

- 2,521 total square feet of living area

- Large living and dining rooms are a plus for formal entertaining or large family gatherings

- Informal kitchen, breakfast and family rooms feature a 37' vista and double bay windows

- Generously sized master bedroom and three secondary bedrooms grace the second floor

- 4 bedrooms, 2 1/2 baths, 2-car garage

- Basement foundation

Second Floor
1,146 sq. ft.

First Floor
1,375 sq. ft.

Single Level Traditional

- 3,412 total square feet of living area

- Large formal dining room with vaulted ceiling is adjacent to the entry foyer

- Expansive sunken great room boasts a dramatic fireplace and vaulted ceiling

- Master bedroom and library are secluded from other living areas

- Family-style kitchen/breakfast area includes pantry and island cooktop

- Sunken master bedroom has patio access and a luxurious private bath

- 3 bedrooms, 3 baths, 2-car side entry garage

- Basement foundation, drawings also include slab foundation

Two-Story Sunken Family Room

- 3,315 total square feet of living area

- Energy efficient home with 2" x 6" exterior walls

- Island kitchen, breakfast room and two-story sunken family room combine for convenient family dining or entertaining

- Two-story foyer opens into bayed formal dining and living rooms

- Master bedroom features a sitting area, large walk-in closet and deluxe bath

- 4 bedrooms, 3 1/2 baths, 2-car side entry garage

- Basement foundation

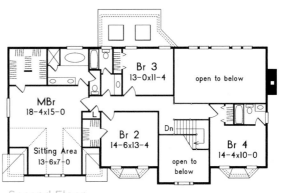

Second Floor
1,620 sq. ft.

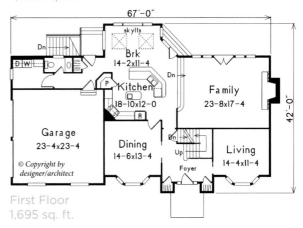

First Floor
1,695 sq. ft.

Features Galore In A Two-Story Home

- 2,828 total square feet of living area

- Multiple gables and wrap-around porch create a classic country exterior

- The spacious entry features a see-through stone fireplace and provides access to the study, guest bedroom and bath, dining room and staircase

- A well-designed kitchen has an island snack bar, built-in pantry and access to porch

- The two-story dining room includes a stone fireplace, master bedroom balcony overlook and 17' high window wall that accesses rear patio

- 4 bedrooms, 2 1/2 baths, 1-car and 2-car rear entry garages

- Basement foundation

Second Floor
1,256 sq. ft.

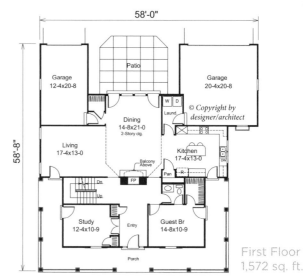

First Floor
1,572 sq. ft.

Country Kitchen Great For Gathering

- 3,782 total square feet of living area

- Stylish staircase in the foyer ascends to the second floor balcony overlooking the great room below

- Lower level includes a media/theater room with built-in bookshelves and component shelving

- The formal dining room is decorated with an impressive tray ceiling drawing the eye upward

- Massive 42″ direct vent fireplace and expansive window wall helps bring the outdoors into the vaulted great room

- 4 bedrooms, 3 1/2 baths, 2-car garage

- Basement foundation

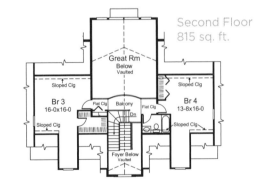

Second Floor
815 sq. ft.

Lower Level
396 sq. ft.

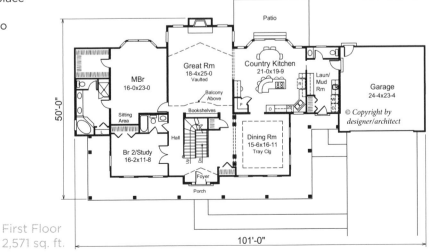

First Floor
2,571 sq. ft.

Exterior Exalts In Imagination

- 3,013 total square feet of living area
- Varying roof lines create an exciting exterior look
- Unique interior has countless innovative features
- Large activity area and hall to laundry area feature a curving window wall that surrounds the outdoor atrium
- Kitchen opens to a sun-drenched nook with a sloped ceiling and skylights
- Master bedroom boasts a luxurious step-up vaulted bath with Roman tub, separate shower/toilet area and an enormous walk-in closet
- 4 bedrooms, 3 baths, 2-car garage
- Partial basement/crawl space foundation

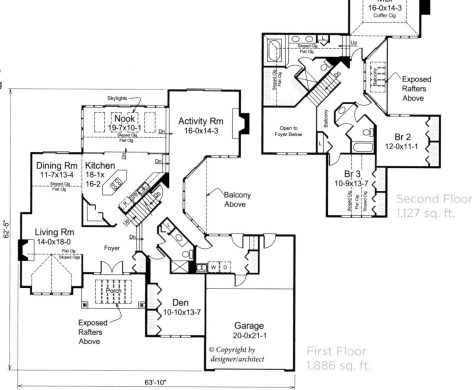

LOWE'S
LEGACY
SERIES

Impressive Exterior, Spacious Interior

- 2,511 total square feet of living area
- Energy efficient home with 2″ x 6″ exterior walls
- Kitchen, breakfast and living rooms feature tray ceilings
- Architectural elements combine to create an impressive exterior
- Master bedroom includes large walk-in closet, oversized bay window and private bath with shower and tub
- 4 bedrooms, 2 1/2 baths, 3-car side entry garage
- Basement foundation, drawings also include crawl space and slab foundations

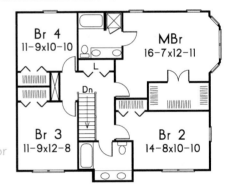

Second Floor
1,174 sq. ft.

Br 4
11-9x10-10

MBr
16-7x12-11

Br 3
11-9x12-8

Br 2
14-8x10-10

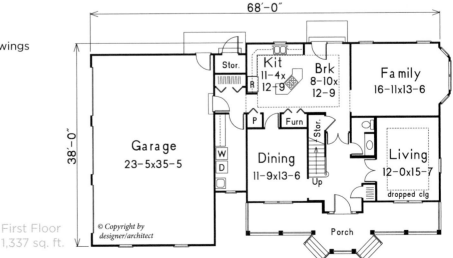

First Floor
1,337 sq. ft.

68′-0″

38′-0″

Garage
23-5x35-5

Kit
11-4x12-9

Brk
8-10x12-9

Family
16-11x13-6

Dining
11-9x13-6

Living
12-0x15-7
dropped clg

Porch

© Copyright by designer/architect

Master Bedroom Is A Luxurious Retreat

- 2,587 total square feet of living area
- High windows above French doors in the great room create a spectacular view
- The spacious kitchen serves the breakfast and dining rooms with ease
- The second floor offers plenty of space with three bedrooms and a storage area
- 4 bedrooms, 3 1/2 baths, 2-car side entry garage
- Basement foundation

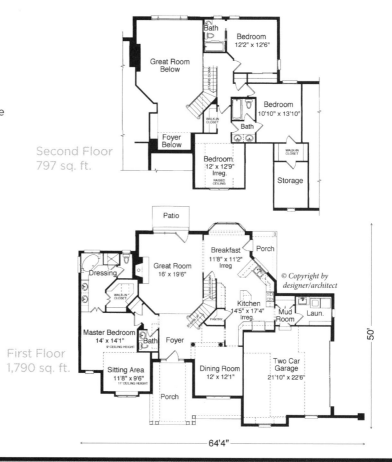

Second Floor
797 sq. ft.

First Floor
1,790 sq. ft.

Bright, Vaulted Spaces

- 2,459 total square feet of living area
- Energy efficient home with 2" x 6" exterior walls
- Kitchen has an open feel with an angled counter to enjoy views through to the family and breakfast rooms
- Secluded master bedroom includes dressing area, access to the outdoors and private bath with tub and shower
- Stylish, open stairway overlooks the two-story foyer
- 4 bedrooms, 2 1/2 baths, 2-car garage
- Basement foundation

Second Floor
598 sq. ft.

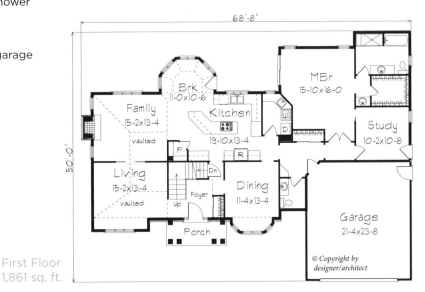

First Floor
1,861 sq. ft.

Craftsman With Stone And Shingle Accents

- 2,953 total square feet of living area

- The chef of the family will be delighted with this gourmet kitchen adjoined by a cozy breakfast room with a computer desk

- A hidden room, cleverly concealed behind cabinet doors is located off the breakfast room providing space for a safe room, storage of valuables or security

- A convenient elevator connects the first and second floors eliminating the vertical challenge of the second floor bedrooms

- 4 bedrooms, 4 baths, 3-car side entry garage

- Basement foundation

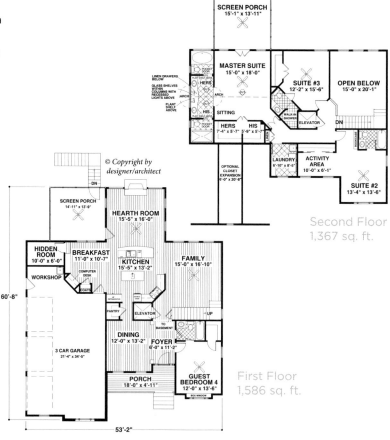

© Copyright by designer/architect

Second Floor
1,367 sq. ft.

First Floor
1,586 sq. ft.

Stately Two-Story

- 3,427 total square feet of living area
- 10' ceilings on the first floor
- Elaborate master bedroom features a coffered ceiling and luxurious private bath
- Two-story showplace foyer is flanked by the dining and living rooms
- Bonus room above the garage is included in the square footage
- 4 bedrooms, 3 1/2 baths, 2-car side entry garage
- Basement foundation

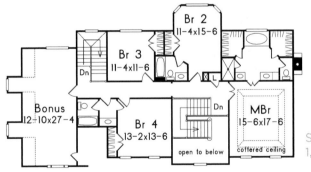

Second Floor
1,874 sq. ft.

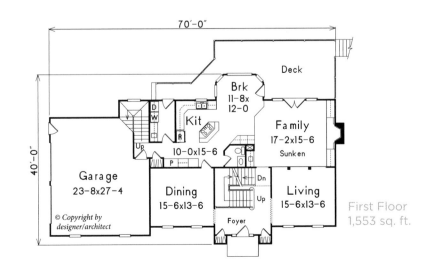

First Floor
1,553 sq. ft.

Luxurious Estate

- 3,978 total square feet of living area
- Stately wood columns and mouldings dress the arched openings that separate the entry, living and dining rooms
- The huge vaulted great room offers a fireplace and ascending wood-crafted staircase with balcony overlook
- The spacious kitchen and breakfast room adjoin a functional mud room with rear stairs to the second floor
- The bonus room on the second floor is included in the square footage
- 4 bedrooms, 3 full baths, 2 half baths, 3-car side entry garage
- Basement foundation

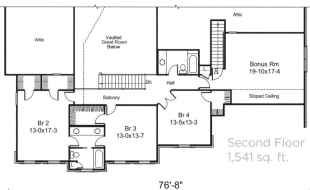

Second Floor
1,541 sq. ft.

First Floor
2,437 sq. ft.

A Touch Of Old-World Charm

- 2,320 total square feet of living area
- From the foyer, there is a panoramic view of the dramatic great room and formal dining room
- A butler's pantry is strategically placed between the formal dining room and casual breakfast room
- French doors add light and style to the breakfast room
- 4 bedrooms, 2 1/2 baths, 2-car garage
- Basement foundation

Second Floor
725 sq. ft.

First Floor
1,595 sq. ft.

Luxury Living Defined

- 2,764 total square feet of living area

- The eye-catching exterior features brick and stone, multiple gables, a cozy porch with railing and rough cedar shake siding

- A grand-sized entry accesses a private parlor with double glass doors, dining room with tray ceiling and a powder room

- The kitchen enjoys a center island, huge walk-in pantry, built-in double oven and features a 50' vista through the breakfast and family rooms

- A vaulted master bedroom with plush bath and two walk-in closets shares the second floor with three additional bedrooms and a Jack and Jill bath

- 4 bedrooms, 2 1/2 baths, 2-car garage

- Basement foundation

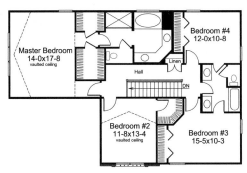

Master Bedroom
14-0x17-8
vaulted ceiling

Bedroom #4
12-0x10-8

Linen

Hall

DN

Bedroom #2
11-8x13-4
vaulted ceiling

Bedroom #3
15-5x10-3

Second Floor
1,332 sq. ft.

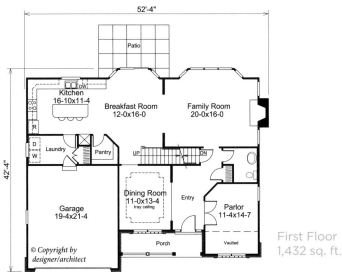

52'-4"

Patio

42'-4"

Kitchen
16-10x11-4

DW

Breakfast Room
12-0x16-0

Family Room
20-0x16-0

D W

R

Laundry

Pantry

UP

DN

Garage
19-4x21-4

Dining Room
11-0x13-4
tray ceiling

Entry

Parlor
11-4x14-7

© Copyright by
designer/architect

Porch

Vaulted

First Floor
1,432 sq. ft.

The Lowe's Legacy Series
Multi-Family

HDA, Inc. is proud to introduce to you the Lowe's Legacy Series. The home plans in this collection carry on the Lowe's tradition of quality and expertise, and will continue to do so for many generations.

Choosing a home plan can be a daunting task. With the Legacy Series, we will set your mind at ease. Selecting a plan from this group will ensure a home designed with the Lowe's standard of excellence, creating a dream home for you and your family.

This collection of Legacy Series plans includes our most popular multi-family home plans. Browse through the pages to discover a multi-family home with the options and special characteristics you need.

Along with one-of-a-kind craftsmanship, all Legacy Series home plans offer industry-leading material lists. These accurate material lists will save you a considerable amount of time and money, providing you with the quantity, dimensions and descriptions of the major building materials necessary to construct your home. You'll get faster and more accurate bids from your contractor while saving money by paying for only the materials you need.

The Lowe's Legacy Series is the perfect place to start your search for the home of your dreams. You will find the expected beauty you want and the functional efficiency you need, all designed with unmatched quality.

Turn the page and begin the wonderful journey of finding your new home.

Photos clockwise from top: 542-008D-0034, page 274; 542-007D-0020, page 243; 542-007D-0024, page 277; 542-008D-0032, page 252.

Elegant Exterior Accents Spacious Design

- 2,885 total square feet of living area
- Cozy study adjoins the master bedroom
- Several windows brighten the main living area
- Practical counterspace in the kitchen overlooks the dining and living areas
- Convenient laundry closet is located on the second floor
- Each unit has 3 bedrooms, 3 baths
- Slab foundation
- Unit A has 1,437 square feet of living space and Unit B has 1,448 square feet of living space

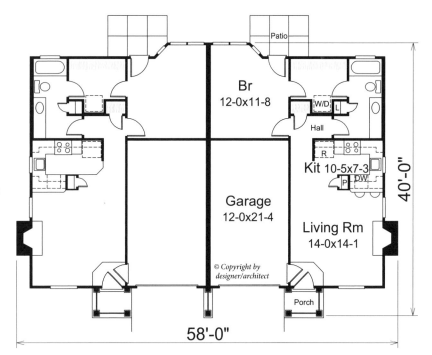

Compact Duplex With Garage

- 1,306 total square feet of living area
- Attractive country exterior with protective porch
- The living room is open to the kitchen and features a 9' ceiling, entry area and fireplace
- The U-shaped kitchen has plenty of cabinets, a built-in pantry and snack counter
- A bay window, full-glass door to a private patio and a large walk-in closet with stacked washer/dryer alcove are a few of the amenities of the bedroom
- Each unit has 1 bedroom, 1 bath, 1-car garage
- Slab foundation
- Each unit has 653 square feet of living area

Patio

Br
12-0x11-8

W/D

Hall

Garage
12-0x21-4

Kit 10-5x7-3

Living Rm
14-0x14-1

Porch

© Copyright by designer/architect

40'-0"

58'-0"

Duplex With Plenty Of Style

- 1,704 total square feet of living area
- Smartly designed layout with emphasis on efficiency
- Functional kitchen embraces the sun with its bay window, glass sliding doors and pass-through to living room
- Five generously designed closets offer an abundance of storage
- Each unit has 2 bedrooms, 1 bath, 1-car garage
- Basement foundation
- Duplex has 852 square feet of living space per unit

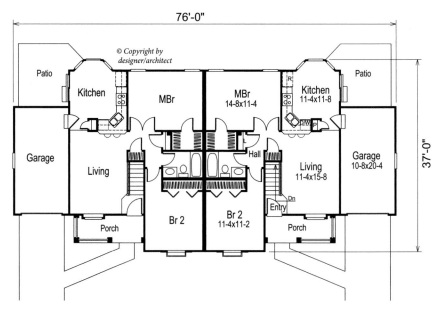

Vaulted Ceilings Add Spaciousness To Living Areas

- 2,318 total square feet of living area
- Great room and dining area are complemented with a fireplace and patio access
- Breakfast bar has a corner sink which overlooks the great room
- Plant shelf graces vaulted entry
- Master bedroom provides walk-in closet and private bath
- Each unit has 3 bedrooms, 2 baths, 1-car garage
- Basement foundation
- Duplex has 1,159 square feet of living space per unit

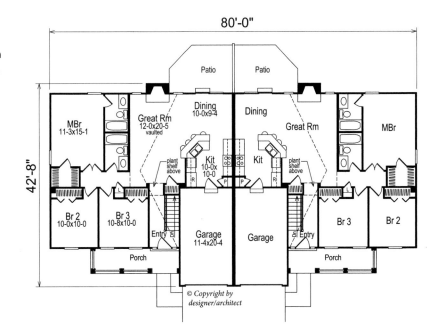

© Copyright by designer/architect

Inviting Entry With Built-In Planter

- 1,966 total square feet of living area
- Energy efficient home with 2" x 6" exterior walls
- Entry opens into main living space or dining area/kitchen
- Ample closet/storage space throughout duplex
- Large L-shaped dining area/kitchen has garage access
- Several windows brighten the living room
- Each unit has 2 bedrooms, 1 bath, 1-car garage
- Basement foundation
- Duplex has 983 square feet of living space per unit

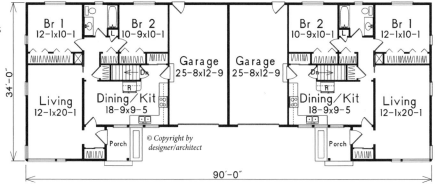

Open Floor Plan Is Perfect For Entertaining

- 2,662 total square feet of living area
- Living room has a vaulted ceiling, built-in bookshelves and a fireplace
- Plenty of storage space is offered in this duplex
- Large bedroom with a private bath and two closets is an ideal master suite
- Each unit has 2 bedrooms, 2 baths, 2-car garage
- Basement foundation, drawings also include crawl space/slab foundation
- Duplex has 1,331 square feet of living space per unit

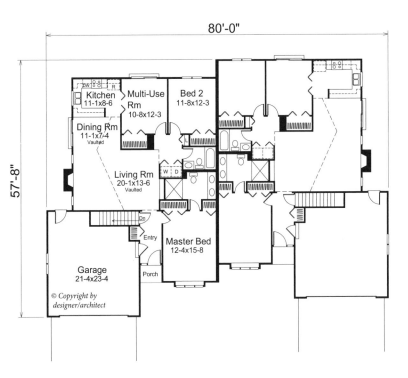

Cozy Duplex Retreat

- 1,076 total square feet of living area

- A country porch for quiet times leads to a living room with fireplace and kitchen/dining area

- The bedroom offers a double-door entry, walk-in closet and a bath with linen closet

- Spacious and private screen porch is steps away from the kitchen/dining area through sliding doors

- Each unit has 1 bedroom, 1 bath

- Crawl space foundation, drawings also include slab foundation

- Duplex has 538 square feet of living space per unit

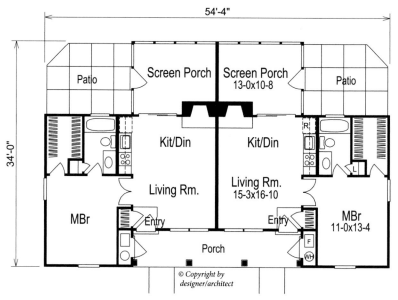

LOWE'S
LEGACY
SERIES

Gracious Living In A Duplex

- 2,088 total square feet of living area

- Each unit has an open living room that enjoys expansive views through two glass sliding doors and has access to a large covered patio

- A snack bar, built-in pantry and abundant cabinets are just a few of the many amenities of the well-designed kitchen

- The master bedroom features a volume ceiling, bright window-wall, walk-in closet, access to bath and a nearby laundry room

- Each unit has 2 bedrooms, 1 bath

- Crawl space foundation, drawings also include slab foundation

- Each unit has 1044 total square feet of living area

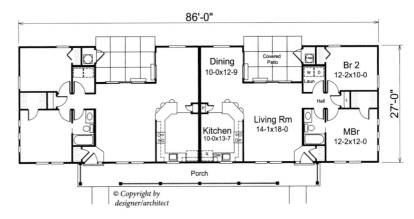

A Duplex With Three Bedroom Units

- 1,938 total square feet of living area
- The large living room is open to the kitchen and features an entry foyer with convenient coat closet
- Glass sliding doors with a view of the side fenced patio, a snack bar and built-in pantry are some of the great bonuses found in the kitchen
- A laundry closet with stacked washer/dryer is located at the end of the hall that accesses the bath, linen closet and three bedrooms
- Each unit has 3 bedrooms, 1 bath
- Slab foundation
- Each unit has 969 total square feet of living area

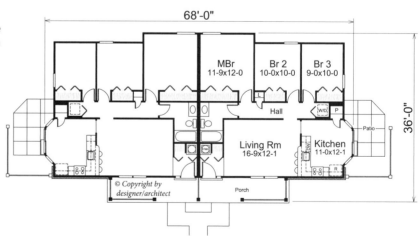

68'-0"

36'-0"

MBr
11-9x12-0

Br 2
10-0x10-0

Br 3
9-0x10-0

Hall

w/d   P

Patio

Living Rm
16-9x12-1

Kitchen
11-0x12-1

R

© Copyright by
designer/architect

Porch

Compact Home With Large Living Room

- 1,536 total square feet of living area
- Living room joins the kitchen/dining area for an open atmosphere
- L-shaped kitchen with outdoor access and convenient laundry area
- Linen and coat closet
- Each unit has 2 bedrooms, 1 bath
- Crawl space foundation, drawings also include slab foundation
- Duplex has 768 total square feet of living space per unit

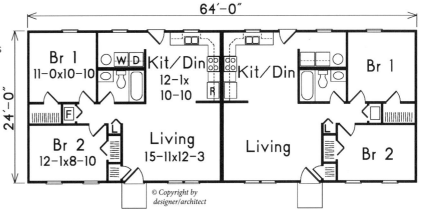

Compact Two-Story Duplex

- 2,408 total square feet of living area

- The large great room offers a fireplace and dining area with view of the patio

- Each unit enjoys its own private garage, front porch and rear patio

- The second floor bedrooms are large in size and feature spacious walk-in closets

- Each unit has 2 bedrooms, 1 1/2 baths, 1-car garage

- Basement foundation

- Duplex has 1,204 square feet of living space per unit

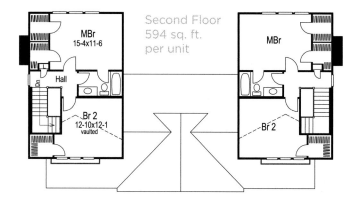

Second Floor
594 sq. ft.
per unit

MBr
15-4x11-6

Hall

Br 2
12-10x12-1
vaulted

MBr

Br 2

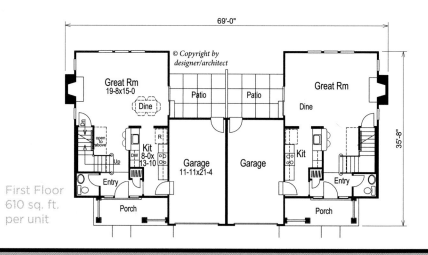

69'-0"

© Copyright by
designer/architect

Great Rm
19-8x15-0

Patio

Patio

Great Rm

Dine

Dine

open
to
above

Kit
8-0x
13-10

Garage
11-11x21-4

Garage

Kit

Entry

Entry

Porch

Porch

35'-8"

First Floor
610 sq. ft.
per unit

LOWE'S LEGACY SERIES

Fourplex With Southern Charm

- 2,840 total square feet of living area
- Living room is graced with a bay window and fireplace
- Kitchen offers efficient layout and overlooks dining area
- Bedroom includes a spacious walk-in closet
- Convenient laundry closet is located off hall
- First floor units have patios and second floor units have decks located off the dining area
- Each unit has 1 bedroom, 1 bath
- Basement foundation
- Fourplex has 710 square feet of living space per unit

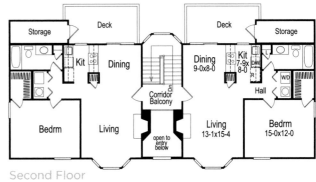

Second Floor
710 sq. ft. per unit

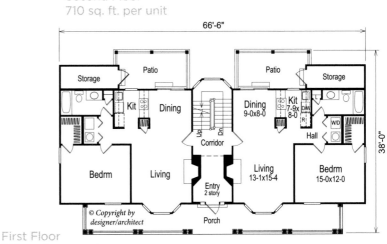

First Floor
710 sq. ft. per unit

© Copyright by designer/architect

Dutch Hip Roof Creates An Attractive Facade

- 3,674 total square feet of living area
- Spacious second floor master bedroom has a large walk-in closet
- Kitchen has a snack counter that opens to the dining area and great room
- Each unit has 3 bedrooms, 2 1/2 baths, 2-car garage
- Basement foundation, drawings also include crawl space and slab foundations
- Duplex has 1,837 total square feet of living space per unit

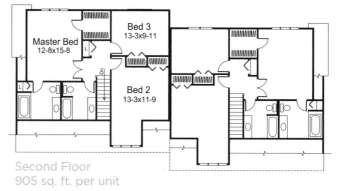

Second Floor
905 sq. ft. per unit

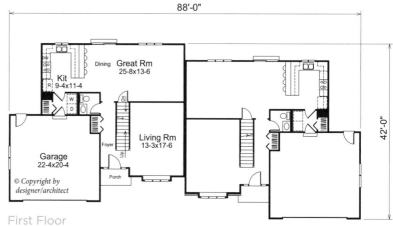

First Floor
932 sq. ft. per unit

© Copyright by designer/architect

Stylish Living, Open Design

- 1,992 total square feet of living area
- Graciously designed ranch duplex with alluring openness
- Vaulted kitchen with accent on spaciousness features huge pantry, plenty of cabinets and convenient laundry room
- Master bedroom includes its own cozy bath and oversized walk-in closet
- Each unit has 2 bedrooms, 2 baths, 1-car garage
- Basement foundation
- Duplex has 996 square feet of living space per unit

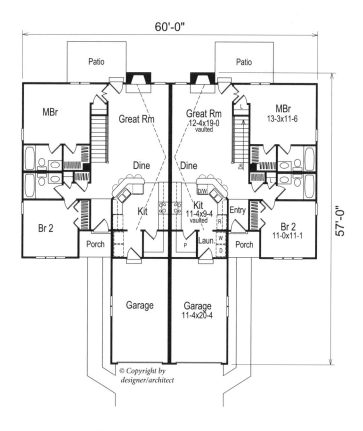

Duplex With A Grand-Scale Country Porch

- 3,502 total square feet of living area

- Two-story entry has an elegant staircase that leads to the living room with a fireplace

- Breakfast room enjoys a bay window, sliding glass doors to outdoor balcony and a pass-through to the kitchen

- A lower level laundry area is provided in each unit

- Each unit has 3 bedrooms, 2 1/2 baths, 2-car drive under garage

- Walk-out basement foundation

- Duplex has 1,751 square feet of living space per unit with 792 square feet on the first floor, 707 square feet on the second floor and 252 square feet on the lower level

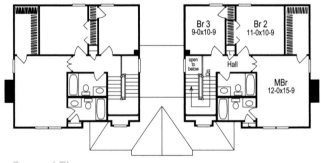

Second Floor
707 sq. ft. per unit

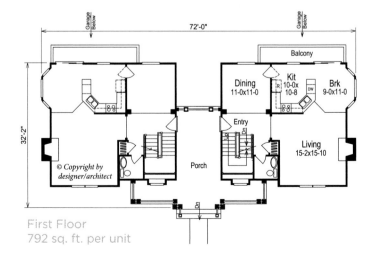

First Floor
792 sq. ft. per unit

Convenient And Open Floor Plan

- 1,966 total square feet of living area
- Lots of storage space throughout
- Oversized kitchen is easy to organize
- Large living room windows allow plenty of sunlight
- Each unit has 3 bedrooms, 1 bath
- Basement foundation, drawings also include crawl space and slab foundations
- Duplex has 983 square feet of living space per unit

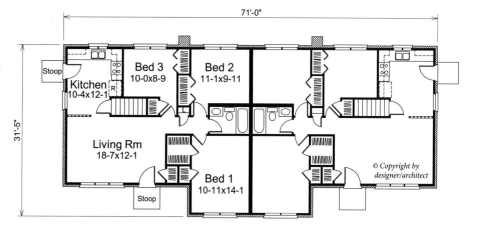

Efficient And Open Duplex Design

- 896 total square feet of living area
- Energy efficient home with 2" x 6" exterior walls
- Small cabin duplex is well suited for rental property or permanent residence
- Compact, yet convenient floor plan
- Well organized for economical construction
- 1 bedroom, 1 bath
- Slab foundation
- Duplex has 448 square feet of living space per unit

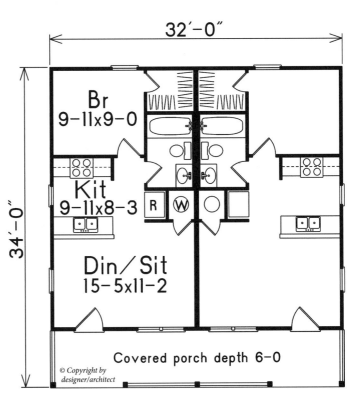

32'-0"

34'-0"

Br
9-11x9-0

Kit
9-11x8-3

R   W

Din/Sit
15-5x11-2

Covered porch depth 6-0

© Copyright by
designer/architect

LEGACY SERIES

Traditional Two-Story Duplex

- 3,056 total square feet of living area

- Multiple gables, hipped roof and an elongated porch all help to create this handsome exterior

- The large living room has a corner fireplace and is open to a very spacious dining area

- A convenient laundry room, built-in pantry and island cabinetry are some of the many amenities of the well-equipped kitchen

- Each unit has 3 bedrooms, 2 1/2 baths, and a 2-car garage

- Crawl space foundation

- Each unit has 749 square feet on the first floor and 779 square feet on the second floor with 1,528 square feet of living space per unit

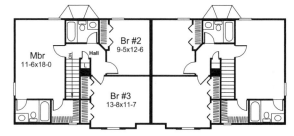

Second Floor
779 sq. ft.
per unit

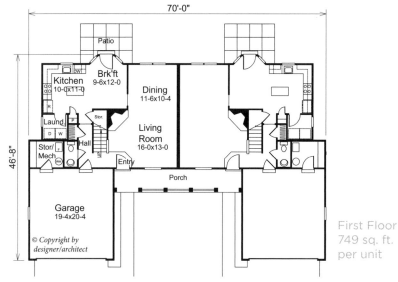

First Floor
749 sq. ft.
per unit

Duplex Fits Well With Neighborhood

- 4,184 total square feet of living area
- Combined kitchen, living and dining rooms create an open living atmosphere
- Handy laundry room and large linen closet on the second floor
- Master bedroom includes a private bath and balcony
- First floor bedroom is an ideal guest room
- Each unit has 4 bedrooms, 3 baths
- Slab foundation
- Duplex has 2,092 square feet of living space per unit with 1,108 square feet on the first floor and 984 square feet on the second floor

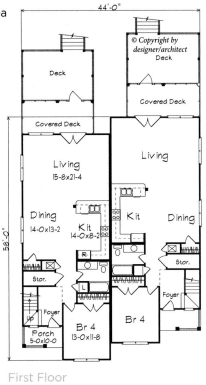

First Floor
1,108 sq. ft.
per unit

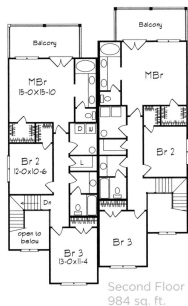

Second Floor
984 sq. ft.
per unit

LOWE'S
LEGACY
SERIES

Well-Designed Facade, Welcoming And Distinctive

- 4,240 total square feet of living area
- Kitchen, brightened by a large bay window, accesses patio on first floor units and deck on second floor units
- Corner fireplace provides warmth and charm
- Bedrooms are separated from living areas for privacy
- Laundry is located off hall for accessibility
- Each unit has 3 bedrooms, 2 baths, 1-car garage
- Basement foundation
- Fourplex has 1,060 square feet of living space per unit

Second Floor
2,120 sq. ft.

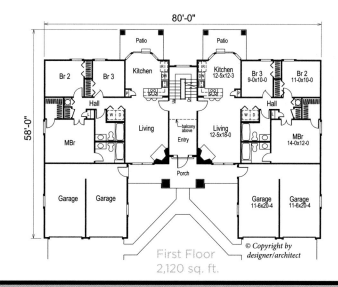

First Floor
2,120 sq. ft.

© Copyright by
designer/architect

Excellent Design Is Traditional And Comfortable

- 4,936 total square feet of living area
- All units have convenient rear access to the patio
- Unit A has 2 bedrooms, 1 bath
- Unit B has 3 bedrooms, 1 1/2 baths
- Basement foundation, drawings also include crawl space/slab foundation
- Unit A has 1,040 square feet of living space and Unit B has 1,428 square feet of living space with 714 square feet on both floors

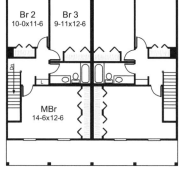

Second Floor Unit B 714 sq. ft. per unit

Br 2
10-0x11-6

Br 3
9-11x12-6

MBr
14-6x12-6

Living Rm
14-6x17-11

Dining Rm
10-6x8-1

Kitchen
10-6x8-0

Family/Dining Rm
20-2x12-5

© Copyright by designer/architect

Living Rm
16-10x12-1

Stoop

Br 2
11-1x15-4

MBr
13-11x12-4

Porch

40'-0"

94'-0"

First Floor
Unit A
1,040 sq. ft.
per unit

First Floor
Unit B
714 sq. ft.
per unit

LOWE'S
LEGACY
SERIES

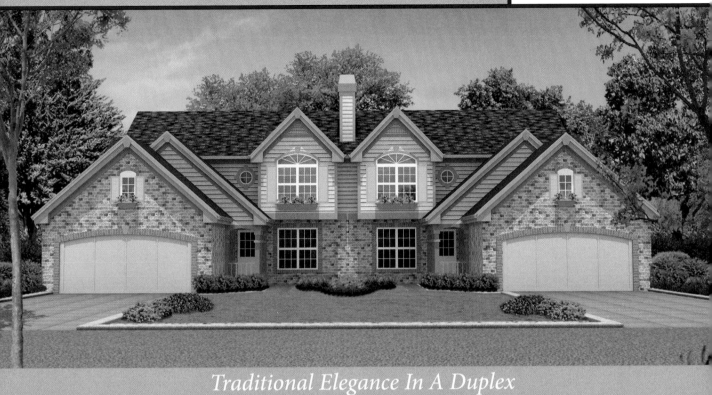

Traditional Elegance In A Duplex

- 3,258 total square feet of living area
- Multi-gables, brickwork, windows with shutters and planter boxes create great curb appeal
- Living room includes a large dining area, fireplace, entry with coat closet and nearby powder room
- Well-equipped kitchen includes an island snack bar, bayed breakfast room, built-in pantry, corner windows above sink and laundry room
- Second floor has large bedrooms including a vaulted master bedroom with luxury bath
- Each unit has 3 bedrooms, 2 1/2 baths, 2-car garage
- Basement foundation
- Duplex has 1,629 square feet of living space per unit

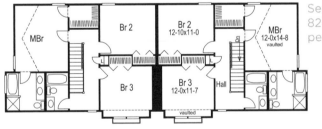

Second Floor
823 sq. ft.
per unit

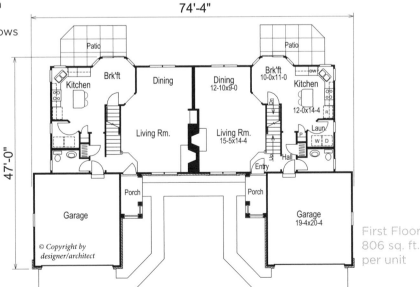

First Floor
806 sq. ft.
per unit

Expansive, Open Space Created By Living Areas

- 2,800 total square feet of living area
- Energy efficient home with 2" x 6" exterior walls
- Large master bedroom enjoys a walk-in closet and private bath with linen area
- Covered entrance opens into entry with coat closet
- Work area in garage
- Convenient laundry room
- Half wall defines the kitchen and opens to the large living room
- Each unit has 2 bedrooms, 2 baths, 2-car garage
- Basement foundation
- Duplex has 1,400 square feet of living space per unit

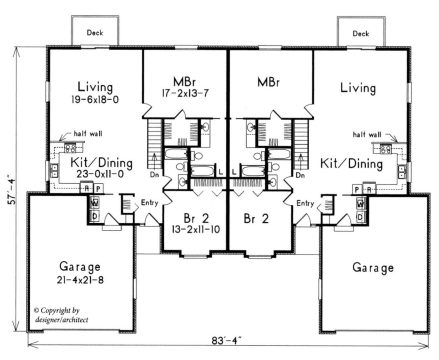

Symmetrical Country Style Duplex With Center Garage

- 1,200 total square feet of living area

- This duplex has an L-shaped kitchen that enjoys a raised eating bar

- The bedroom includes plenty of closet space and access to a covered or optional screen porch

- The kitchen includes space for a stacked washer and dryer

- Each unit has a total of 600 square of living area

- 1 bedroom, 1 bath, 1-car garage per unit

- Crawl space foundation, drawings also include slab foundation

Covered Or Optional Screen Porch 10 x 6

Covered Porch 20 x 6

Kitchen 12-6 x 9 Range

Bath

Bedroom 12 x 12-6

Garage 13 x 23

© Copyright by designer/architect

Garage 13 x 23

Kitchen 12-6 x 9 Range

Covered Porch 20 x 6

Covered Or Optional Screen Porch 10 x 6

Bath

Bedroom 12 x 12-6

Step

Stacked Washer/ Dryer

R

Stacked Washer/ Dryer

R

Raised Bar

Raised Bar

Bonus Room 12 x 7-4

Living Room 18 x 11 8-0 C.H.

Fireplace or Gas Logs

Fireplace or Gas Logs

Living Room 18 x 11 8-0 C.H.

Bonus Room 12 x 7-4

Covered Porch 30 x 6

Width : 86'-0"
Depth: 32'-0"

Covered Porch 30 x 6

Duplex Sporting A Prairie Style

- 2,040 total square feet of living area
- Two family home offers a large covered porch, stucco exterior, transom windows 30" roof overhang and an attractive roof dormer to deliver great looks
- The large living room has a 10' volume ceiling, separate entry with guest closet and is open to a pass-through kitchen
- A snack bar, corner sink, laundry and mechanical closets and glass sliding doors to the rear patio are the many features of the country kitchen
- Each unit has 2 bedrooms, 2 baths
- Slab foundation
- Each unit has 1,020 square feet of living area

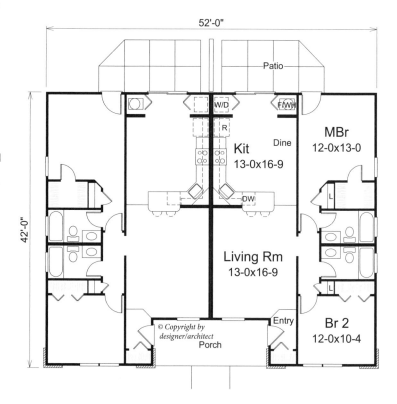

52'-0"

42'-0"

Patio

W/D

F/WH

R

Kit
13-0x16-9

Dine

MBr
12-0x13-0

DW

Living Rm
13-0x16-9

L

L

© Copyright by designer/architect

Entry

Br 2
12-0x10-4

Porch

Multi-Family With Residential Look

- 2,901 total square feet of living area
- This fiveplex home features an extra-large porch and roof dormers that make it fit graciously into any residential neighborhood
- Three first floor units have access to their own balcony while the two lower level units each enjoy private patios
- Each unit has 1 bedroom, 1 bath
- Walk-out basement foundation
- Units A and C each have 600 square feet of living area, Unit B has 517 square feet of living area and Units D and E each have 592 square feet of living area

62'-0"

40'-0"

First Floor

Balcony | **Balcony** | **Balcony**

Brk'ft | Bedroom | Bedroom 10-1x11-0 | Kit 9-2x13-7 | Bedroom 11-1x10-0 | Brk'ft 9-0x8-9

Kit | Hall | Hall | Hall | Kit 9-0x9-3

Living Rm. 14-0x11-6

Living Rm. 16-7x11-3

Living Rm

Entry | Entry | Entry

© Copyright by designer/architect

Porch

Unit A
600 sq. ft.

Unit B
517 sq. ft.

Unit C
600 sq. ft.

Lower Level

Patio | Patio

Brk'ft | Bedroom | storage | storage | Bedroom 11-1x10-0 | Brk'ft 9-0x8-9

Kit | Hall | storage | Hall | storage | Kit 9-0x9-3

Hall | storage | storage | Hall

storage | Laundry

Living Rm. | Living Rm. 16-0x10-8

utility

Unit D
592 sq. ft.

Unit E
592 sq. ft.

Unique Duplex Style, Easily Fits In Neighborhood

- 1,924 total square feet of living area
- Large bedrooms have plenty of closet space
- Unit A features ranch-style living and has 792 total square feet of living area
- Unit B is a 1 1/2 story and has 1,132 square feet of living area with 575 square feet on the first floor and 557 square feet on the second floor
- Unit A has 2 bedrooms, 1 bath
- Unit B has 2 bedrooms, 1 1/2 baths
- Basement foundation

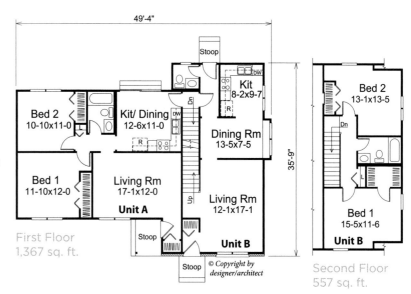

© Copyright by designer/architect

First Floor
1,367 sq. ft.

Second Floor
557 sq. ft.

Fourplex With Multi-Gabled Facade

- 7,372 total square feet of living area
- Units A and D feature living/ dining combination and master bedroom retreat with lower level family room and third bedroom
- Units A and D include 3 bedrooms, 3 baths, 2-car garage in a ranch plan with 1,707 square feet of living area with 1,149 on the first floor and 558 on the lower level
- Units B and C feature luxurious living area and second floor with spacious master bedroom featuring two walk-in closets and a lavish bath
- Units B and C include 3 bedrooms, 2 1/2 baths, 2-car garage in a two-story plan with 1,979 square feet of living area with 1,055 on the first floor and 924 on the second floor
- Basement foundation

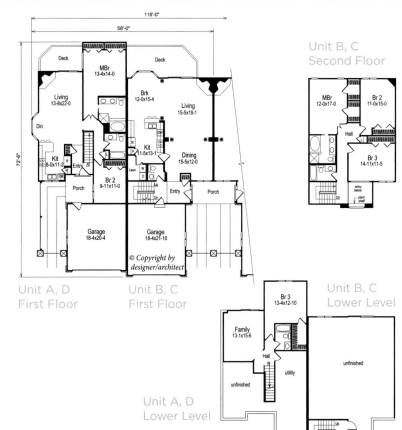

Atrium Duplex With Room To Grow

- 3,484 total square feet of living area
- Inviting porch and foyer lead to the vaulted living room/dining balcony with atrium window wall
- Bedroom #2 doubles as a study with access to the deck through sliding glass doors
- Atrium opens to the large family room and third bedroom
- Each unit has 3 bedrooms, 2 baths, 2-car garage
- Walk-out basement foundation
- Duplex has 1,742 square feet of living space per unit

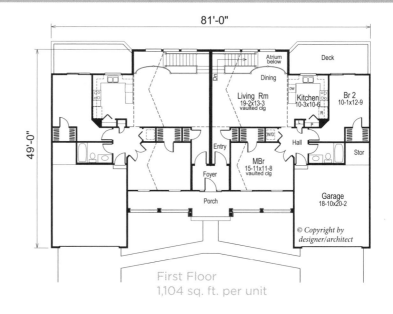

First Floor
1,104 sq. ft. per unit

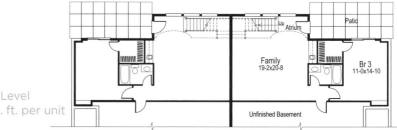

Lower Level
638 sq. ft. per unit

LOWE'S
LEGACY
SERIES

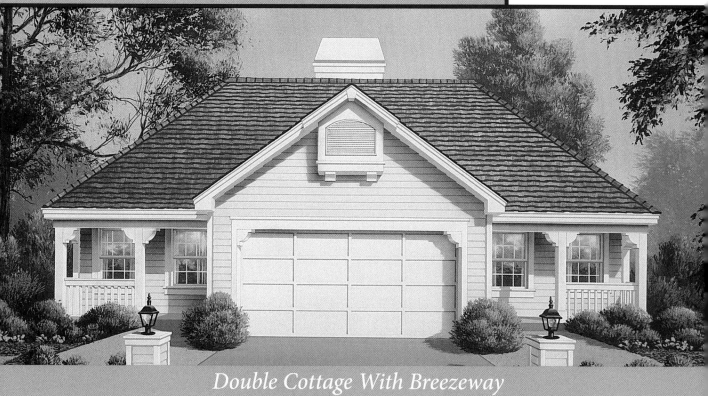

Double Cottage With Breezeway

- 844 total square feet of living area

- Unique design with maximum privacy for each unit featuring its own porch, breezeway entrance and large sundeck

- Living room offers separate entry with closet, fireplace, sliding glass doors to deck and opens to dining area with bay window

- The bedroom features a private bath, closet and views to porch

- Each unit has 1 bedroom, 1 bath, shared 2-car garage

- Crawl space foundation

- Duplex has 422 square feet of living area per unit

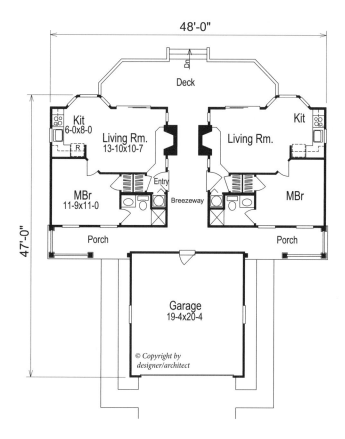

Delightful Duplex With Trendsetting Style

- 2,602 total square feet of living area
- A spacious courtyard with decorative columned lanterns invites you into a large private covered veranda at the entry
- The huge living room has a fireplace, convenient access to the rear patio, a dining area and separate entry with coat closet
- A snack bar for four, a built-in pantry and abundant cabinets and counter space are a few outstanding features of the well designed kitchen
- The master bedroom has sliding glass doors to the rear patio, a large walk-in closet and luxury bath
- 2 bedrooms, 2 baths per unit
- Slab foundation
- Each unit has 1,301 square feet of living area

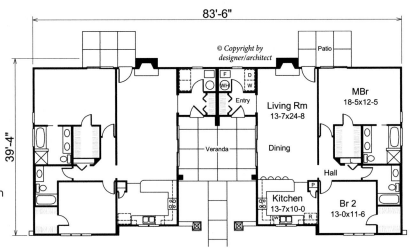

Easily Converts To Duplex Unit

- 1,044 total square feet of living area
- Great layout for narrow lot
- Master bedroom includes a walk-in closet, dressing area and private entrance to bath
- Convenient entrance from garage into main living area
- Kitchen includes an island cooktop, stackable washer/dryer closet and adjacent dining area with patio access
- Living room boasts a cozy corner fireplace
- Each unit has 3 bedrooms, 1 bath, 2-car garage
- Slab foundation

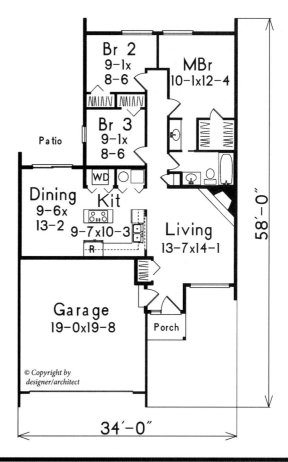

Duplex Residence With Appeal

- 2,030 total square feet of living area
- Each home has a wrap-around porch that welcomes you into a spacious living room with a feature arched window and planter box
- The cozy U-shaped kitchen with built-in pantry is open to the breakfast room with a bright cheery bay window
- Double entry doors, private bath and walk-in closet are the features of the roomy master bedroom which has access to a rear patio
- 2 bedrooms, 2 baths per unit
- Slab foundation
- Each unit has 1,015 total square feet of living area

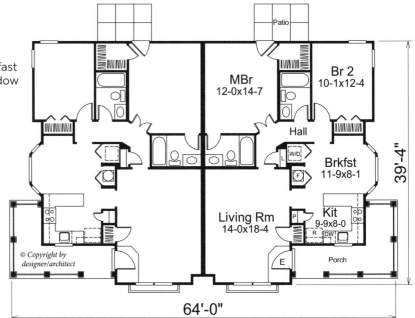

Patio

MBr
12-0x14-7

Br 2
10-1x12-4

Hall

Brkfst
11-9x8-1

© Copyright by designer/architect

Living Rm
14-0x18-4

Kit
9-9x8-0

Porch

39'-4"

64'-0"

Delightful Ranch Duplex

- 1,626 total square feet of living area
- Energy efficient home with 2″ x 6″ exterior walls
- Each unit features a lovely front porch that enters to find a coat closet and spacious living room
- The large eat-in kitchen offers plenty of space for dining and accesses the side yard
- The full bath includes a double-bowl vanity for ease of sharing
- Each unit has 2 bedrooms, 1 bath
- Slab foundation
- Duplex has 813 square feet of living space per unit

© Copyright by designer/architect

64'-0"

27'-6"

Kit 11-10x11-4
Br 2 11-2x11-4
Br 2 11-2x11-4
Kit 11-10x11-4

Living 14-1x11-4
Br 1 11-10x14-10
Br 1 11-10x14-10
Living 14-1x11-4

Porch 7-10x3-6
Porch 7-10x3-6

Fourplex Is Spacious With Large Living Room

- 3,648 total square feet of living area
- The large kitchen is adjacent to the living room
- Handy linen closet in hallway
- Spacious living room has easy access to patio or balcony
- Centrally located laundry closet for stackable washer and dryer
- Each unit has 2 bedrooms, 1 bath
- Crawl space foundation, drawings also include slab foundation
- Fourplex has 912 square feet of living space per unit

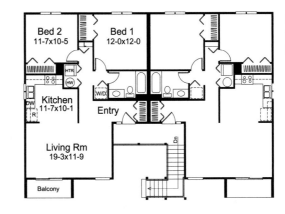

Second Floor
912 sq. ft.
per unit

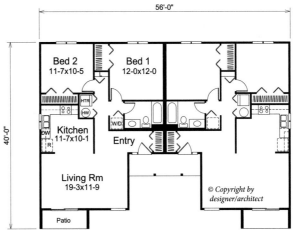

First Floor
912 sq. ft.
per uint

© Copyright by
designer/architect

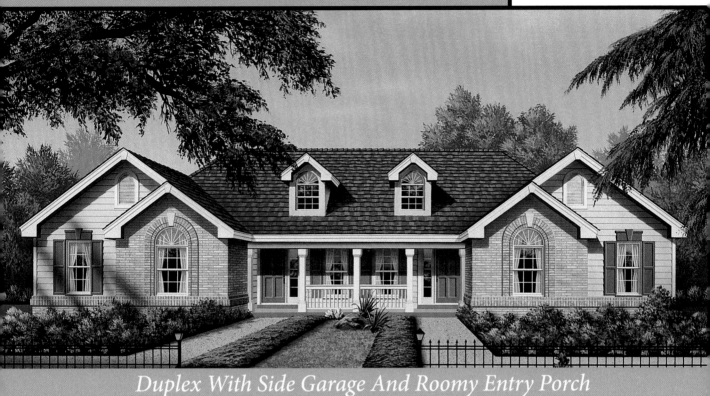

Duplex With Side Garage And Roomy Entry Porch

- 1,700 total square feet of living area
- Front facade fits splendidly with residential surroundings
- Well-planned kitchen includes an abundance of cabinets
- Spacious bedroom with double closets
- Plant shelf, open stairway and vaulted ceilings highlight living space
- Convenient entrance from garage into main living area
- Dining room accesses deck
- Each unit has 2 bedrooms, 1 bath, 1-car side entry garage
- Basement foundation
- Duplex has 850 square feet of living space per unit

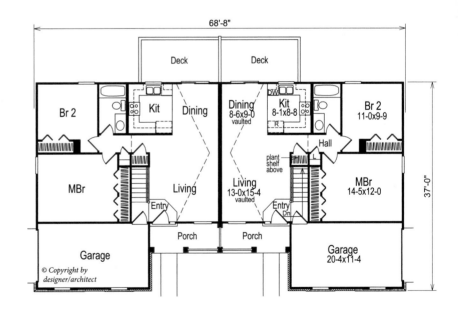

A Fourplex With Distinction

- 2,986 total square feet of living area

- Beautiful stonework with planter boxes and large country porch provide a dazzling exterior

- First floor units have access to their own sundecks while lower level units each enjoy a private patio

- Each unit features a hookup for a stacked washer and dryer

- Units A and B have 2 bedrooms, 1 bath and Units C and D have 1 bedroom, 1 bath

- Walk-out basement foundation with centrally located storage area

- Fourplex has 1,574 square feet of living area on the first floor and 1,412 square feet of living area on the lower level

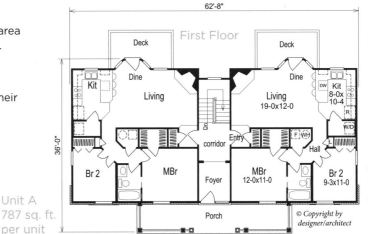

First Floor

Unit A
787 sq. ft.
per unit

Unit B
787 sq. ft.
per unit

© Copyright by designer/architect

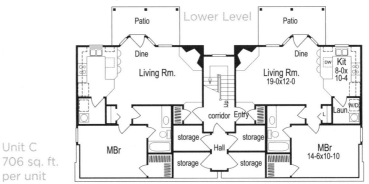

Lower Level

Unit C
706 sq. ft.
per unit

Unit D
706 sq. ft.
per unit

Country Charm In A Double Feature

- 2,986 total square feet of living area
- Vaulted great room, kitchen and two balconies define architectural drama
- First floor master bedroom boasts a lavish bath and double walk-in closets
- Impressive second floor features two large bedrooms, spacious closets, hall bath and balcony overlook
- Each unit has 3 bedrooms, 2 1/2 baths, 2-car garage
- Basement foundation
- Duplex has 1,493 square feet of living space per unit

Second Floor
533 sq. ft.
per unit

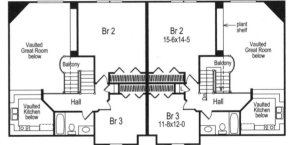

First Floor
960 sq. ft.
per unit

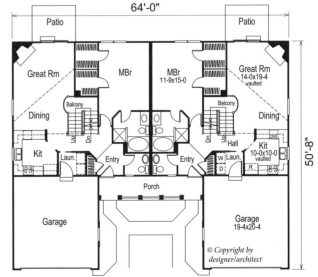

Duplex With Comfortable Lifestyle

- 1,618 total square feet of living area

- Each home has a large covered porch that welcomes you into a separate entry with guest closet and a 1-car garage space with large storage shelf

- The living room with bayed dining area and adjacent U-shaped kitchen defines the spacious, open living area

- A large laundry room with coat closet and a built-in pantry are conveniently located near the kitchen

- The master bedroom is generously sized and features a bath and walk-in closet

- Each unit has 2 bedrooms, 2 baths with shared 2-car garage

- Crawl space foundation, drawings also include slab foundation

- Each unit has 809 square feet of living area

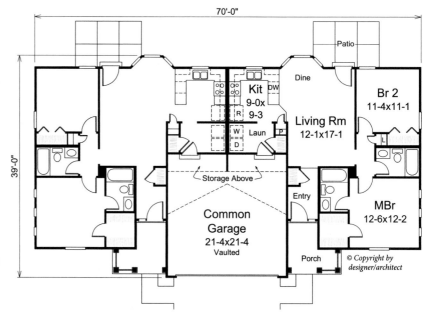

70'-0"

39'-0"

Patio

Dine

Kit
9-0x
9-3

DW

R

W
D   Laun

P

Living Rm
12-1x17-1

Br 2
11-4x11-1

L

Storage Above

Entry

Common Garage
21-4x21-4
Vaulted

MBr
12-6x12-2

Porch

© Copyright by designer/architect

Two-Family Home With Class

- 2,008 total square feet of living area
- Immersed in light, the living room has a luxury entrance foyer with full-glass double entry doors, two large windows and convenient coat closet
- A snack counter, built-in pantry and laundry closet are a few features of the kitchen that opens to the breakfast room with bay and sliding doors to the rear patio
- The master bedroom offers an 11' volume ceiling with a special window wall, exterior planter box for flowers and an extra closet in addition to a walk-in closet
- 2 bedrooms, 2 baths per unit
- Slab foundation
- Each unit has 1,004 total square feet of living area

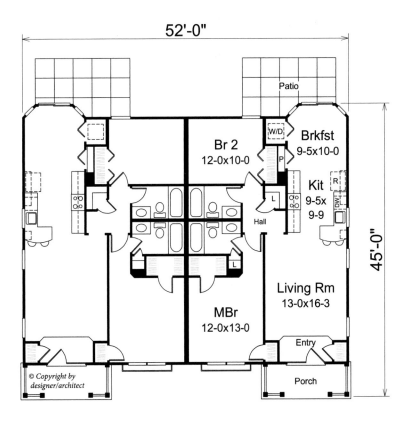

Tudor Influences Enhance This Duplex

- 1,352 total square feet of living area
- See-through fireplace from the living room into the bedroom makes a lasting impression
- Covered front porch is perfect for relaxing evenings
- Galley-style kitchen is compact but well organized for efficiency
- Each unit has 1 bedroom, 1 bath
- Slab foundation
- Duplex has 676 square feet of living space per unit

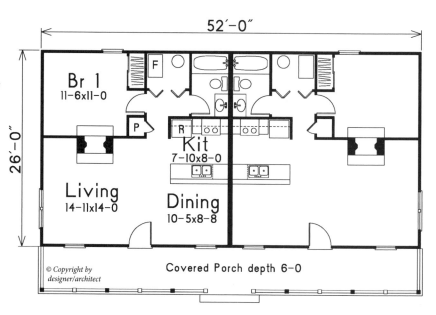

FREE *Lowe's Gift Card Offer*

Lowe's Special Rebate Offer

Purchase any plan package featured in this book PLUS at least $15,000 of your materials from Lowe's and receive a gift card for the purchase price of your plans.

To receive the rebate:

1. Purchase any of the plan packages in this publication PLUS at least $15,000 of the materials to build your home at Lowe's before 12/31/13. Requests must be postmarked by 1/31/14. Claims postmarked after this date will not be honored.

2. Limit one gift card per set of plans.

3. Please allow 3-4 weeks for processing. If you do not receive a gift card after 4 weeks, visit www.lowes.com/rebates, or you may call 1-877-204-1223.

4. Please keep a copy of all materials submitted for your records.

5. Copy the entire sale receipt(s), including store name, location, purchase date, and invoice number, showing blueprint purchase and total amount spent.

6. Mail this complete page with your name, address and other information below, along with a copy of the receipt(s).

Name _____

Street Address _____

City _____

State/Zip _____

Daytime phone number (_____) - _____

E-mail address _____

Plan number purchased 542-_____

I purchased a ☐ One-Set Plan Package
☐ Five-Set Plan Package
☐ Eight-Set Plan Package
☐ Reproducible Masters
☐ Builder's CAD Package

MAIL TO:
Lowe's Free Gift Card Offer
P.O. Box 3029
Young America, MN 55558-3029

Check the status of your rebate at www.lowes.com/rebates

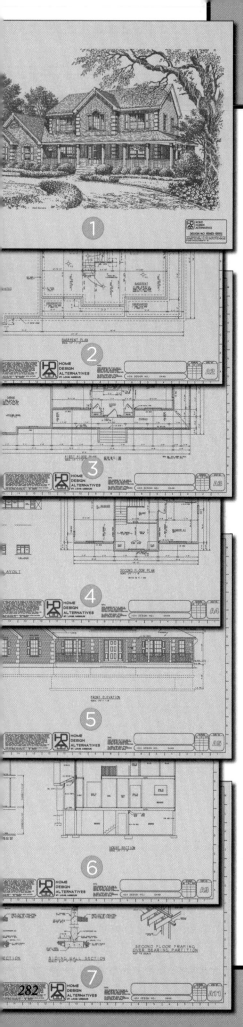

Our Blueprint Packages Include...

Quality plans for building your future,

with extras that provide unsurpassed value,

ensure good construction and long-term enjoyment.

A quality home - one that looks good, functions well, and provides years of enjoyment - is a product of many things - design, materials, and craftsmanship.

But it's also the result of outstanding blueprints - the actual plans and specifications that tell the builder exactly how to build your home.

And with our BLUEPRINT PACKAGES you get the absolute best. A complete set of blueprints is available for every design in this book. These "working drawings" are highly detailed, resulting in two key benefits:

- Better understanding by the contractor of how to build your home and...

- More accurate construction estimates.

1. *Cover Sheet* is the artist's rendering of the exterior of the home and is included with many of the plans. It will give you an idea of how your home will look when completed and landscaped.

2. *Foundation* plan shows the layout of the basement, crawl space, slab or pier foundation. All necessary notations and dimensions are included. See the plan page for the foundation types included. If the home plan you choose does not have your desired foundation type, our Customer Service Representatives can advise you on how to customize your foundation to suit your specific needs or site conditions.

3. *Floor Plans* show the placement of walls, doors, closets, plumbing fixtures, electrical outlets, columns, and beams for each level of the home.

4. *Interior Elevations* provide views of special interior elements such as fireplaces, kitchen cabinets, built-in units and other features of the home.

5. *Exterior Elevations* illustrate the front, rear and both sides of the house, with all details of exterior materials and the required dimensions.

6. *Sections* show detail views of the home or portions of the home as if it were sliced from the roof to the foundation. This sheet shows important areas such as load-bearing walls, stairs, joists, trusses and other structural elements, which are critical for proper construction.

7. *Details* show how to construct certain components of your home, such as the roof system, stairs, deck, etc.

Now that you've found the home you've been looking for, here are some suggestions on how to make your Dream Home a reality. To get started, order the type of plans that fit your particular situation.

Your Choices

□ *The One-Set Study Package* - We offer a One-set plan package so you can study your home in detail. This one set is considered a study set and is marked "not for construction." It is a copyright violation to reproduce blueprints.

□ *The Minimum 5-Set Package* - If you're ready to start the construction process, this 5-set package is the minimum number of blueprint sets you will need. It will require keeping close track of each set so they can be used by multiple subcontractors and tradespeople.

□ *The Standard 8-Set Package* - For best results in terms of cost, schedule and quality of construction, we recommend you order eight (or more) sets of blueprints. Besides one set for yourself, additional sets of blueprints will be required by your mortgage lender, local building department, general contractor and all subcontractors working on foundation, electrical, plumbing, heating/air conditioning, carpentry work, etc.

□ *Reproducible Masters* - If you wish to make some minor design changes, you'll want to order reproducible masters. These drawings contain the same information as the blueprints but are printed on reproducible paper and clearly indicates your right to alter, copy or reproduce. This will allow your builder or a local design professional to make the necessary drawing changes without the major expense of redrawing the plans. This package also allows you to print copies of the modified plans as needed. The right of building only one structure from these plans is licensed exclusively to the buyer. You may not use this design to build a second or multiple dwelling(s) without purchasing another blueprint. Each violation of the Copyright Law is punishable in a fine.

□ *Mirror Reverse Sets* - Plans can be printed in mirror reverse. These plans are useful when the house would fit your site better if all the rooms were on the opposite side than shown. They are simply a mirror image of the original drawings causing the lettering and dimensions to read backwards. Therefore, when ordering mirror reverse drawings, you must purchase at least one set of right-reading plans. Some of our plans are offered mirror reverse right-reading. This means the plan, lettering and dimensions are flipped but read correctly. See the Home Plan Index on page 285-286 for availability.

□ *PDF File Format* - A complete set of construction drawings in an electronic format that allows you to resize and reproduce the plans to fit your needs. Since these are electronic files, we can send them to you within 24 hours (Mon-Fri, 8-5 CST) via email and save you shipping costs. They also offer printing flexibility by allowing you to print the size and number of sets you need.

Note: These are not CAD files and cannot be altered electronically.

□ *CAD Packages* - A CAD package is a complete set of construction drawings in an electronic file format. They are especially beneficial if you have a significant amount of changes to make to the home plan you have selected or if you need to make the home plan fit your local codes. If you purchase a CAD Package, you have the option to take the plan to a local design professional who uses AutoCAD or DataCAD and they can modify the design much easier and quicker than with a paper-based drawing, which will help save you time and money. Just like our reproducible masters, with a CAD package you will receive a one-time build copyright release that allows you to make changes and the necessary copies needed to build your home. For more information and availability, please call our Customer Service Department at 1-877-379-3420.

Your Blueprint Package will contain the necessary construction information to build your home. We also offer the following products and services to save you time and money in the building process.

Material List

Material lists are available for all of the plans in this book. Each list gives you the quantity, dimensions and description of the building materials necessary to construct  your home. You'll get faster and more accurate bids from your contractor while saving money by paying for only the materials you need. See your Commercial Sales Specialist at your local Lowe's Store to receive a free take-off.

Note: The material list is designed with the standard foundation only and does not include alternate or optional foundations.

Express Delivery

Most orders are processed within 24 hours of receipt. Please allow 7-10 business days for delivery. If you need to place a rush order, please call us by 11:00 a.m. Monday through Friday, 8am-5pm CST and ask for express service (allow 1-2 business days).

Technical Assistance

If you have questions, call our technical support line at 1-314-770-2228 Monday through Friday, 8am-5pm CST. Whether it involves design modifications or field assistance, our designers are extremely familiar with all of our designs and will be happy to help you. We want your home to be everything you expect it to be.

Other Great Products...

Below are a few products sure to help the beginner as well as the experienced builder.

Legal Kit

Home building can be a complicated process with many legal regulations being confusing. This Legal Kit was designed to help you avoid many legal pitfalls and build your home with confidence using the forms and contracts featured in this kit. Included are  request for proposal documents, various fixed price and cost plus contracts, instructions on how and when to use each form, warranty statements and more. Save time and money before you break ground on your new home or start a remodeling project. Instructions are included on how to use the kit and since the documents are universal, they are designed to be used with all building trades. Since review by an attorney is always advised before signing any contract, this is an ideal way to get organized and started on the process. Plus, all forms are reproducible making it a terrific tool for the contractor and home builder. At a price of $35.00, this kit is ideal.

Detail Plan Packages
Framing, Plumbing and Electrical Plan Packages

Three separate packages offer home builders details for constructing various foundations; numerous floor, wall and roof framing techniques; simple to complex residential 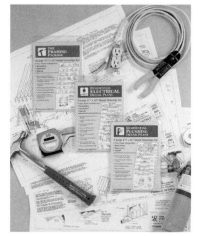 wiring; sump and water softener hookups; plumbing connection methods; installation of septic systems, and more. Packages include 3-dimensional illustrations and a glossary of terms. These drawings do not pertain to a specific home plan making them perfect for your building situation.

Each package is $20 or purchase all three for $40 making it a great bargain.

To order any of the products on this page, please see the Home Plan order form on page 288.

Before You Order

Exchange Policies

Since blueprints are printed in response to your order, we cannot honor requests for refunds. However, if for some reason you find that the plan you have purchased does not meet your requirements, you may exchange that plan for another plan in our collection within 90 days of purchase. At the time of the exchange, you will be charged a processing fee of 25% of your original plan package price, plus the difference in price between the plan packages (if applicable) and the cost to ship the new plans to you.

Please note: Reproducible drawings can only be exchanged if the package is unopened. PDF and CAD files are not returnable and non-refundable.

Building Codes & Requirements

At the time the construction drawings were prepared, every effort was made to ensure that these plans and specifications meet nationally recognized codes. Our plans conform to most national building codes. Because building codes vary from area to area, some drawing modifications and/or the assistance of a professional designer or architect may be necessary to comply with your local codes or to accommodate specific building site conditions. We advise you to consult with your local building official for information regarding codes governing your area.

Additional Sets†

Additional sets of the plan ordered are available for an additional cost of $45.00 each. Five-set, eight-set, and reproducible packages offer considerable savings.

† Available only within 90 days after purchase of plan package or reproducible masters of the same plan.

Blueprint Price Schedule

Price Code	1-Set	**SAVE $80** 5-Sets	**SAVE $115** 8 Sets	PDF File/ Reproducible Masters	CAD
AAA	$310	$410	$510	$610	$1,000
AA	$410	$510	$610	$710	$1,250
A	$470	$570	$670	$770	$1,370
B	$530	$630	$730	$830	$1,490
C	$585	$685	$785	$885	$1,600
D	$635	$735	$835	$935	$1,700
E	$695	$795	$895	$995	$1,820
F	$750	$850	$950	$1,050	$1,930
G	$1,000	$1,100	$1,200	$1,300	$2,130
H	$1,100	$1,200	$1,300	$1,400	$2,320
I	$1,150	$1,250	$1,350	$1,450	$2,420
J	$1,200	$1,300	$1,400	$1,500	$2,650
K	$1,250	$1,350	$1,450	$1,550	$2,900

Plan prices are subject to change without notice.
Please note that plans and material lists are not refundable.

Shipping & Handling Charges

U.S. Shipping - (AK & HI express only)	1-4 Sets	5-7 Sets	8 Sets or Reproducibles
Regular (allow 7-10 business days)	$15.00	$17.50	$25.00
Priority (allow 3-5 business days)	$35.00	$40.00	$45.00
Express* (allow 1-2 business days)	$50.00	$55.00	$60.00
Canada Shipping (to/from)**			
Standard (allow 8-12 business days)	$35.00	$40.00	$45.00
Express* (allow 3-5 business days)	$75.00	$85.00	$95.00

Overseas Shipping/International -

Call, fax, or e-mail (plans@hdainc.com) for shipping costs.
 * For express delivery please call us by 11:00 a.m. Monday-Friday CST
** Orders may be subject to custom's fee and/or duties/taxes.

NOTE: Shipping and handling charges do not apply on PDF files.
Orders will be emailed within 24 hours (Mon-Fri., 8-5 CST) of purchase.

Questions? Call Our Customer Service Number
1-877-379-3420

Many of our plans are available in CAD.
For availability, please call our Customer Service Number above.

Order Form

1.) *Call* toll-free 1-877-379-3420 for credit card orders. Mastercard, Visa, Discover and American Express are accepted.

2.) *Fax* your order to 1-314-770-2226.

3.) *Mail* the Order Form to: *HDA, Inc.*
944 Anglum Road
St. Louis, MO 63042
attn: Customer Service Dept.

4.) *Visit* your Commercial Sales Specialist at your local Lowe's store.

For fastest service, Call Toll-Free
1-877-379-3420 day or night

Order Form

Please send me -

PLAN NUMBER 542-_____

PRICE CODE_____ *(see pages 285-286)*

Specify Foundation Type *(see plan page for availability)*

☐ Slab   ☐ Crawl space   ☐ Pier

☐ Basement ☐ Walk-out basement

☐ Reproducible Masters $ _____

☐ PDF File $ _____

☐ Eight-Set Plan Package $ _____

☐ Five-Set Plan Package $ _____

☐ One-Set Study Package *(no mirror reverse)* $ _____

☐ CAD Package *(call for availability)* $ _____

Additional Plan Sets† *(see page 286)*

☐ ____ (Qty.) at $45.00 each $ _____

Mirror Reverse† *(see page 283)*

☐ Right-reading $150 one-time charge
   (see index on pages 285-286 for availability) $ _____

☐ Print in Mirror Reverse
   (where right-reading is not available)

____ (Qty.) at $15.00 each $ _____

☐ Legal Kit *(002D-9991, see page 284)* $ _____

Detail Plan Packages: *(see page 284)*

☐ Framing ☐ Electrical ☐ Plumbing $ _____
(002D-9992) (002D-9993) (002D-9994)

SUBTOTAL $ _____

Sales Tax *(MO residents add 7%)* $ _____

☐ Shipping / Handling *(see page 287)* $ _____

TOTAL *(US funds only - sorry no CODs)* $ _____

I hereby authorize HDA, Inc. to charge this purchase to my credit card account (check one):

☐ MasterCard   ☐ VISA   ☐ DISCOVER   ☐ American Express Cards

Plan prices are subject to change without notice.
Please note that plans and material lists are not refundable.

Credit Card number _____

Expiration date _____

Signature _____

Name_____
(Please print or type)

Street Address_____
(Please do not use a PO Box)

_____

City _____

State _____

Zip _____

Daytime phone number   (_____) - _____

E-mail address _____

I am a ☐ Builder/Contractor

☐ Homeowner

☐ Renter

I ☐ have ☐ have not selected my general contractor.

Thank you for your order!

†Available only within 90 days after purchase of plan package or reproducible masters of same plan.
Note: Shipping and handling does not apply for PDF files. Orders will be emailed within 24 hours (Mon.-Fri., 8am-5pm CST) of purchase.